Madocks

Madocks

A Novel

by
John Idris Jones

ALUN BOOKS
Port Talbot
2012

ISBN 978-0-907117-97-1

Published by
Alun Books, 3 Crown Street, Port Talbot SA13 1BG

Set in 10/12pt Zapf Elliptical

Typeset and Printed in Great Britain by
Andreas Haaf & Son, Port Talbot
Bound by Pughs Colourprint, Port Talbot

Dedication

In memory of my dear late mother Margaret Maude Jones, originally of Tan-y-Dderwen, Minffordd, Penrhyndeudraeth; my grandparents of that address and of Cilan, Borthygest; and all those who contributed to Madocks' Great Scheme, including my great, great, great grandfather, Richard Williams, blacksmith of Tremadog.

Acknowledgment

Some of the information and events in this book are taken from *Madocks and the Wonder of Wales* by Elizabeth Beazley (Faber & Faber, 1967). The author wishes to thank Mrs D. C. R. Walters for her support. Thanks are also due to Alun Jones of Abergele, for superb work in genealogy.

Chapter 1

*A*unty May had occupied her flat in Rhos-on-Sea since her husband died prematurely and she set out on a long break with much travelling. From the other side of the room, next to the door, the picture of William Madocks looked at me. May was wheeling in a trolley. On it she had a teapot, sugar in a bowl, a small jug of milk, a plate of sandwiches and a plate of scones. For a ninety-something-year-old, she did pretty well. She had had a hip operation at the age of ninety-one.

"Tea with milk," she said, giving me a straight look.

I was sitting in the armchair.

"Please," I replied. "And the ham." She knew I liked ham.

She handed me the tea, moving a small table to put it on. Her hands were firm, bony across the back, with brown splotches. She wore a wedding-ring boasting three large diamonds. She had on a skirt of mid blue and a grey cardigan. She was always well-dressed. Her white hair was newly styled, with neat curls.

She turned towards the coffee-table, picking up a small magazine. It was that of the Festiniog Railway Company, Porthmadog.

"They send it to me every six months," she said. "They've asked me to go there. But it's too far. I'd need a lift in a car, there and back."

"I'd take you," I replied with some caution.

"No. Too far. They know where I am. They know who my grandmother's brother was."

At that she straightened, running her hand over her hair. Her shoulders opened. Her slate-blue eyes shone.

Her grandmother's brother was William Williams, Superintendent of Railways, Festiniog Railway, 1876 to 1906 (bardic name Gwilym Meirion). His father, another William Williams, had been with the Railway when it started in Porthmadog in 1836. His father, Richard Williams, blacksmith, who worked for Madocks, was one of the first artisans to occupy a business space in the new town of Tremadog. Another of Richard's sons was Porthmadog blacksmith and inventor John Williams, bardic name Ioan Madog, winner of many prizes for poetry and included in The Oxford Book of Welsh Verse. A distinguished lineage.

She turned towards the portrait of William Alexander Madocks and asserted, "If it had not been for him, we would not be here, and none of this would have happened."

My maternal family were as a fruitful vine growing around the stem of a tree. That tree, its base and roots, was Madocks.

The portrait on the wall seemed to smile at her. Under his benign face, his neckerchief was long and carefully knotted. It was reminiscent of rural days when horses were tethered together by rope and harness; of embankments holding the tides; of trains and carriages with their couplings; of pulleys on sailing-boats firmly holding against the perils of long journeys.

Aunty May died at the age of one hundred. Her last gesture, in the local hospital, was her arm in the air, waving at me. It was as if some two hundred years of family history, the story of the Williamses, beginning with a farmer of Pen Morfa and his talented son Richard was waving at me, demanding attention.

Chapter 2

That first time, William Madocks came alone. He had felt that he had something to settle; something to resolve. He felt a tension inside which needed some dealing with. He did not know what it was. He did not know, as he later surmised, that it was something to do with destiny.

It was not usual for him to be alone. He had a gregarious personality. His time at Oxford was peppered with entertainments. He did not neglect his studies, he was getting on well with his tutor and on his staircase (the steps in wood worn by the tread of dozens of the young, the lazy and the vigorous) he was well liked. His friends gathered around his fireplace with drinks of port, sherry and claret from his well-chosen glasses. Outside his mullioned windows, towards evening, a sharp shout of 'Will, Will,' could be heard as two of his friends urged him to join them at an inn where food and drink flowed easily. He loved conviviality. He loved conversation. Quick repartee, the reply and the sudden burst of laughter, were his world. The light-coloured stone of his Oxford college was his appropriate setting: he was a son of a successful lawyer, offspring of the Welsh-English Madockses.

And then there was the *Dolmelynllyn* episode ('Dolly' as they called it). It was a preamble. The house was of stone, overlooking a sharp valley to the north of Dolgellau, and immediately he saw it, he wanted to change it. He invited his friends down and they all had a good time. They walked the valley of the Ganllwyd and enjoyed the Mawddach. But with his father gone and the inheritance of £50,000, to be spent according to the instructions of trustees, William being one, on freehold property, it was tempting to look for an estate property that would be his home. He also inherited £5,000 in stock; £2,000 in ready cash along with his father's chambers in Lincoln's Inn and the Middle Temple with their books. Also, his inheritance included a holding in an iron smelting factory near Wrexham, which later he was to put to good use. He had tired of Dolly. It had no scope. It was a house for holidays but little more. The games and dramas and poems enacted there were mere entertainments, flimsy and social, and were now things of the past. A bigger stage was called for.

This time, he was alone in the carriage, with his coachman up front. It was the end of the century and it was a glorious early Spring. Daffodils burst out of the hedgerows. Grass was newly growing, its feathery top about to turn into stout growth. Snowdrops scattered their benevolence. And this time, he had come direct. It was as if he had a purpose, a direction, but he did not fully know what it was.

Their last overnight stop, travelling from Oxford, was the Royal Oak at Betws-y-Coed. He had enjoyed it. He was treated well. The horses were stabled; Jack was put up somewhere round the back near the stables and was smiling the following morning. It was a quiet night; he had slept well. As he pulled on his breeches and adjusted his cuffs, he felt what he was, a lucky young man, a man of the world. His breakfast of porridge, eggs and bacon was very agreeable, as was the smile of the serving girl, with her tawny complexion and glowing dark hair.

The turning to the left at Capel Curig caused the carriage to tilt. No problem with the horses, however. They were steadfast. They had sensed that the long gradual upwards gradient from Betws-y-Coed was about to change. He glanced out of the window. The view was spectacular, the valley below, the surrounding hills. And the light had changed; it was now wider, bolder, more silvery. It was now downwards. Soon the road narrowed, clinging to the hillside, heavy with overhanging branches, twisting, turning. Below him was the magnificent Nantgwynant. To his right was Snowdon. Before him on the valley floor was Llyn Gwynant, with its edge following the road. The horses were in good shape and it was as if they enjoyed this jaunt into the distant west, walking this different but congenial setting. Then to the left was Llyn Dinas, more enclosed than its sister lake, squashed between hills, deeper, somewhat forbidding. Madocks was enjoying this journey. The landscape had all his imagination could use: scale, texture, change, grandeur; colours which were complementary, all as one. And still the two horses prevailed, lifting their strong legs as if they were heading for somewhere worth arriving at.

He glanced upwards to the Hill of Emrys where old Welsh folk-tale tradition said two dragons fought, one red, one white. Perhaps it was so in him. His Welsh side and his English side. But the partisan was not his style; he was for conciliation and co-operation. He wanted people to get on together.

To his left the River Glaslyn flattened out, running left and right between stones. Then stone cottages edged the road, some with steps of slate before their doors.

"Jack," he shouted. "Slow down."

Jack was drawing the reins. He looked around. He had a fine nose.

"We need to think about this," said William. "This is about as far as it gets."

They had, of course, noticed the deteriorating condition of the road. In places the carriage and horses were jolted as a wheel hit a stone.

"We'll see where we can put up," he said, looking past Jack's black coat to the overhanging hillsides.

They moved slowly forwards.

"Wait," said William. "I'll ask this man."

He leaned out and addressed a man of middle age. "Is

there somewhere to stay? An inn?" he said. The man looked at him. He shook his head.

He tried again, "An inn. For the night. And the horses."

The man looked up again, shaking his head.

William understood. The man had not a word of English.

He smiled. From his stock of Welsh words he selected one.

"*Diolch*," he said, with a fair competence of pronunciation.

The man raised his head and smiled. As the carriage moved on, he was waving his arm.

They rounded a corner and Beddgelert appeared before them. A stone building faced the river and the old bridge. It had a double front door inside a slate-floored step-up platform from which two pillars rose. The sash windows were freshly painted and the granite walls were grouted with light plaster. Daffodils grew at the corners of the building.

"Turn in," shouted Madocks. "This is it."

He instructed Jack to make the horses secure and to go in and ask for accommodation for the night. He sat there for a few minutes, hearing the river sing as it ran under the bridge. Jack appeared, "Very good sir. One night stay. And dinner. Fine."

Jack was a good companion. He was sturdy, with a good command of English, a loud, clear voice (needed when you had to talk over the sound of horses and wheels in motion) and an open, optimistic, personality. William had known some carriers who were surly as dumb animals, reluctant to do anything except take your money and grumble. But Jack was a find. Give him a good plate of pie and a pint of ale and he was happy. He enjoyed the company of others. Often William had to prompt him out of the back tap room of an inn, where he was in full flow of conversation about something he knew little or nothing about such as French people, the engineering of bridges, or the preparation of food.

William had to admit that he had feelings about this location, which he was a little ashamed of. He felt it was foreign and a little unpleasantly so. He felt he was abroad with a vengeance. There was something in the air; there was a quietness around him. The normal feeling of co-respondence was diminished in him. He was apprehensive. However, his sense of enjoyment in things was intact. His bags were taken, his room was neat and clean. Jack and the horses were looked after. He had a good glass of ale in his hand. He was not much of a smoker but on this occasion he took his pipe and tobacco downstairs. He sat placidly making up his pipe, pressing down and lighting up. As the smoke rose, he noticed two men sitting with their backs to the wall. One leaned forward towards the fire. He had grey eyebrows and high cheekbones. As he drew on his pipe, William noticed a large signet ring on his right hand.

"Going west tomorrow?" the man enquired. His voice was English.

"Yes," William replied. And then he said again "Yes," a little more tentative this time.

"Bloody difficult," the man said.

"Oh?" said William enquiringly.

"Get yourself there at the right time. Otherwise, you're in trouble. One time my chaise had its wheels half in water. But the four horses were strong. They pulled us out. But we'd have been gone . . . " He paused, contemplating death by drowning.

The man continued, as if he sensed that the young pleasant man who had just sat down and was drawing on his pipe was interested in property. "I hear William Price of Rhiwlas is selling-up. The estate consists of eight holdings. A total rent income of some two hundred and twenty pounds. But he's having difficulty in selling up. This sea problem is starving the area. You can't get the sheep to market. It's all a matter of high and low tides. The estate has eight holdings, the smallest being Ynys Fadog." He seemed very well informed and he spoke with the tones of a lawyer or land agent.

Perhaps, thought William, I am here at the right time.

"Do you think the place is worth buying?"

"It could be," the man replied evenly. "It depends what you bring to it. It requires new thinking. It needs somebody with determination and ambition to make something of it. There is plenty of potential. The right person could make a good job of it." At this remark, the man looked at William intently.

He enjoyed his meal. The cheese was very good, as was the wine. He wondered how they had managed to serve such good wine, so far into Wales. The butter was a little over-salted but the bread was excellent, with thick crust. Service was via the lady of the house, thick-set but not inelegant, her arms strong from much boiling and ponching of clothes in the wash. She wore wide, narrow spectacles, as was the fashion now. Her shoes were home-made. A cobbler, he thought, is an excellent thing: good hands, strong thread, made to fit. An analogy for how things should be. Walk down the road and get a pair of shoes made. And on the way, call into the bakery where a floury man in a heavy cotton apron would punch and batter in the early morning to bring out of the coke (and local wood) oven a piece of man's finest, a loaf of bread. Butter, bread, milk and eggs, thought WM, what else do you need? And all local, tied to the land. You cultivate your farm, he thought, and you benefit, live and prosper. But you need money to buy other products too, he thought, as he looked at the tobacco in his pipe, and the fine cotton of his shirt.

The man of the house was stout. A Mister Owen. He was called that by his wife when she was hard-pressed and he a little short of applied vigour.

"Will you get the horses and hitch the carriage," she

instructed the following morning. And in a louder voice, "Mister Owen!"

His head emerged; a faint voice said "Yes", and, fainter "Diawl".

Jack looked pleased. "Very good food," he announced strongly. "Three courses. A good place to stay."

William addressed Mr Owen, "We are obliged to you, Sir. The stay has been a satisfactory one. Now back to the road and the trusty horses."

Having received the payment in his hand, the innkeeper touched his forehead in thanks. "Perhaps you will stay again, Sir. We don't get many visitors here."

With that plaintive remark in his ears, William turned to his carriage and stepped in.

They were settled to the journey again. The black and the grey in unison. The Pass of Aberglaslyn took them in. The road worsened. The road was practically in the river, which was quickening and deepening. Tall fir trees blocked out the sun. Above them stone slabs glistened. Trees and shrubs were growing out of the vertical rock. It was like Austria or Switzerland. The Glaslyn was barely fifteen feet across, its energy increasing as its girth shrank. Before them was a bridge carrying the road westwards towards Ffestiniog. Opposite it was a stone cottage. An old man was enjoying the sun close to its front door. William recalled his previous encounter with a native but decided to try his luck, instructing Jack to pull up the horses. He leaned out and said "Good morning." He then remembered the Welsh for it and said, "Bore da." The old man looked puzzled and pleased. "Bore da; bore da; bore da," he repeated in a surprisingly strong voice.

"Can I get over Traeth Mawr?" asked William.

"No," the old man replied with gusto, "no, not now. Tide up."

This was bad news because William had planned to go over and turn left into Lleyn.

"Tide up," said William, puzzling. "No way over?"

"No. No way over," said the man, his English improving as William spoke.

"Well," said William, "we shall have to see." The explorer in him was aroused. *"Diolch yn fawr,"* he said, remembering his stock of Welsh phrases.

"Diolch yn fawr," echoed the old man, laughing, his worn teeth showing, *"a paid a boddi."*

The last remark William didn't understand and Jack certainly didn't. It meant, 'don't drown.' But drowning was not in William's nature.

They proceeded. The road became a track. The carriage swung from side to side. Every now and then the horses slipped.

Suddenly the crack in the sky between the rocks broke open. Slowly they traversed. Another corner was rounded and the sky opened again. Then a gradual curve. William had his head out of the window. The carriage came to a slow halt. It did not need him to cry, 'Halt.' Jack sat upright in his seat. The horses had drawn to a halt; they raised their hoofs slowly.

Before them was a scene of such spectacular impact that the two men sat silent for at least four minutes. Practically at their feet, certainly at the base of the carriage wheels, was seawater. It went on and on in a long blue blanket of gentle wave and ripple until it hit the horizon in a clear line some three miles distant. It was interrupted by small islands of grass and shrub. To the left, a family of swans travelled in unison. To the right, a heron dipped its long neck in the rushes. Newly-hatched small brown geese scuttered around fallen branches, paddling furiously. The fields to the right sloped up directly from the water. Across the background, the low mountains of Lleyn and Eifionydd lay as bumps across the horizon. To the right the mini-Alps of Snowdonia serrated the sky in a series of peaks. To his left, tree-covered slopes of slate and earth dipped into the sea. The hump of

Moel-y-Gest rose some two miles away directly ahead, seawater lapping its lower reaches. It was set on Ynys-y-Towyn, an island at high tide. On it he could see a few cottages.

The river had joined the sea. Afon Glaslyn had come to its fulfilment. It finished in a territory of wide promise, of unexplored significance. Its name meant blue lake, and this was it.

He opened the door of the carriage, stepped out, and stood inches away from the water's edge. Then he looked at Jack and smiled. A strange sense of something in the future flowed through him. He raised his right arm. With his right hand he traced a shape in the Spring air. His fingers started to the right then moved around towards Ynys-y-Towyn; then they moved leftwards following the line of the horizon. As his hand moved across this line, he was pressing harder. Then, pointing to the far left, his hand made a small circular motion. This continued upwards and to the left, stopping at the slate-rich Moelwyn mountains above Ffestiniog.

Then he placed his left hand in his pocket. He looked to the right, to the sheep and lambs on the fields, neatly separated by stone hand-made walls. He observed a distant farmhouse, set halfway up a hill, above the blue lake.

His left hand felt the stout folded schedule. It was from his father's legal office, listing his inheritance. He bent his fingers around the paper. He looked again at the farmhouse. He saw its rectangular shape and the grey stone of its walls. He noted the overgrown hillside in front of it, dropping to the estuary. He recognised the potential of the house and its spectacular setting. He identified with its location: it was set similar to Fron Yw, his childhood home in the Vale of Clwyd. He had a sense of things to come. He, Jack, horses and carriage, had to re-trace their steps. But William Alexander Madocks was changed. His face took on a new look: tighter, more focused. His vigour swelled in him. He was set on a new course. In him was the birth of a grand idea.

Chapter 3

William Thomas reflected that there was something good and pleasing in the sound and sight of pigs. He had his hand on the stout door of one of the sties. Below him, two miles away, Traeth Mawr lay as a blue blanket. Two pigs were inside, rolling against one another, nudging, provoking, making that deep rumbling-grunting which is a music of the satisfied. They needed cleaning out; pigs always needed cleaning-out, but you have to stop sometimes and let the muck build up; he'd step inside about twice a week and perform the task; the manure pile grew next to the sty and when the weather was suitable, it was forked on to the cart, carried to the field and spread about. The top fields needed more than the bottom fields, on account of the thinness of soil and more stones. His sheep lived mostly on these top fields, his stock increasing each year. On the lower fields his eighteen milking cows had a contented time, trundling in to his milking parlour twice a day, as his voice carried to them and they came to him in a slow ritual of rhythmical movement of legs and heads. Now that things had expanded, he could not do all this on his own and he was appreciative of the help of his son Richard.

He was proud of his farm. It was originally of sixty-five acres when he bought it from Ann Rowland in 1779. Ann had been widowed and the farm had run down. There was little alternative for her; she was childless, with no husband, and the farm relied on the income from sheep. Ysgubor Goch was his. He had placed his money on the table at the time when Ann's will was read. Her small benefactions ten shillings here, a pound there were read out, the few faces around the table not much cheered, and the positive note came when

William reached into his breeches pocket, taking out a wad of five pound notes and sovereigns.

His son Richard was three at the time. After the sale, Margaret set to scrub and brush. The detritus of forty years was swept away. The old stove was still intact and Margaret, who was an excellent cook, soon had her two males heartily eating good quality food. Pigs were essential. Hams hung from hooks in the ceiling. Potatoes were plentiful and after the old hens were replaced, a supply of eggs was assured.

Ysgubor Goch was an improving farm. William soon bought more land. He now had over a hundred acres and was beginning to experiment with cereals. His oats were coming on well and wheat was needed by two millers on the Criccieth road.

As he stood by the pigs he looked over to Ynyscynhaearn, the old church this side of Moel-y-Gest. He hoped that they would not find their way in to that cemetery soon, not before his farm was fully matured and his son married with children.

Below him, the Glaslyn was flowing and the blue lake filling-out. Each day he noticed a change. One day the fresh water would flow this way, other days it would flow that way. Small islands formed and were then swept away. There was a daily clash between fresh water and salt water. The sea flowed in and where the two came together, there were eddies and whirlpools. His eye turned leftwards, in the direction of Snowdon. A few miles away, a movement caught his eye. He saw horses, one black, one grey. He saw a dark smudge which must have been a carriage and he thought he saw movement beside it, possibly a man standing. He did not know it but facing one another, some three miles apart, were two ambitious men with land and improvement on their minds.

Chapter 4

It was 1795: William Madocks had inherited. It was a balance between the loss of his father and the very substantial gain in income. He missed his father, who had taken on the role of King's Counsel, but in the last ten years or so he had become more and more remote, spending more time at Lincoln's Inn. He had a house in Bedford Row, where the boys were born, William in 1773, but William preferred countryside and his family's ancestral acres in North Wales. In the early days, there had been a happiness in the roundness of the family, father, mother, brothers (John Edward and Joseph) all in *Fron Yw*, the tall house which stood up against the eastern edge of the Clwyd valley rather like a boat swept out of the sea by a westerly wind and left, high and dry. But even though it was a little forbidding, the house was a happy one. As a small boy he tried his hand at tennis, thrashing and swiping at the leather ball. He enjoyed pony-riding in the fields below the house, dodging the oaks and elms; this was close to being dangerous. He was always a goer, jumping and testing himself, full of vigour. He recalled his mother's voice, 'William. William.' She standing at the edge of the drive, shouting, her voice sweetly carrying over the fields towards Denbigh. He was often late for family meals; he had been engaged in something, bedding the ponies, keeping the dogs away from the sheep, feeding the new calves with Trefor the farmer. He was a capable lad. He had little time for brooding, for sulking, or tears. He was a maker and survivor from an early age. Activity came naturally to him. As his father steadily scratched away in his office, with its oak door and brass handle, his lad tumbled about with a determination and activity which belied the paper-work, the accounting, the careful activities of the Law.

His father became more and more successful, more and more remote. Moving to Llay Hall, near Wrexham, was no pleasure for young William. It had been in the family since an earlier William Madocks, great-grandfather of the present one, settled in Ruthin and made a fortune in tobacco. William's activities were curtailed in this narrow valley with limited light, compared with the majestic openness of the Vale of Clwyd. There was no farm to explore, swing about in, pat the cows. This house was larger and grander. There were servants for each activity. One of them, an Englishman called Albert, had a nasty temper; he had narrow eyes and a ginger beard.

"Oxford," said his father to him one day. "I'll have a chat with my friends at All Souls." This seemed very ambitious, but his father was set on it. His two brothers were at Harrow. They came home in suits and polished shoes. William wished he was back in Fron Yw, where the Madocks family had deep roots.

Tutors came and the boy learned quickly. Handwriting and composition he excelled in but with Mr Hoover he was good at Maths too, calculating in three columns with the speed of an accountant. His eleventh birthday was celebrated with some of his friends in the large dining-room, with its silver candlesticks and portrait of his grandfather. His mother was good at events and celebrations; she was always well-dressed and showed a way with servants which was firm but not overbearing. "To William," his friend Jake announced, raising his glass. "To William," the others repeated. He had good friends.

He was sent to Charterhouse, the boarding school in the heart of London. The regime there was not much to his liking. The food was plain, plenty of bread and cheese but none of the Welsh lamb and beef he was used to. He survived at the school and perhaps it did give him a sense of how to get by despite circumstances. Although a slow grower, he excelled at games. His drilling in Latin and Greek was relentless; but one day he blotted his copy-book. He went missing. He left the school premises with three of his friends without telling anybody. This was strictly against school rules, and in this school rules were everything. They slipped through a back gate of the school next to the vegetable garden when the gardener was out of sight.

They looked in hatters' windows, decided against sitting in a dark corner of a pub in case they were recognised in their school outfits and in Pall Mall admired the shiny carriages, wealthy men in tall hats, the pavement sellers of hot chestnuts. William was feeling hungry. A young lady came before him, saying, "Fancy a stroll, young man?" He was startled. He turned his face away. "No thank you." He had no money in his pocket and he was wondering how he could get something to eat.

His absence soon came to the ears of his father in Lincoln's Inn, his clerk having written him a note, placing it on his desk. His misdemeanour was not long-lasting. He found the streets losing their appeal and, feeling hungry and dejected, the four of them headed back to school. For this, during December, 1789, William was sent down from school, expelled. His penalty for a brief period of freedom had been swift and harsh. But that was the nature of the school and its regime. They felt they had to set an example to others who wanted to escape its rigours, who wanted to please themselves rather than obey its rules. This episode brought about what a cousin in a letter described as a 'paper war' between John Madocks and the school.

Three months before his seventeenth birthday, William was up at Oxford. Christ Church was congenial, not too strict, not too liberal. Young men of the nobility as well as commoners studied and played while in France the Revolution continued its bloody course.

Regularly, he slipped over to Wales. The North Wales gentry were well to his tastes, and he was related to some of them. Sir Watkin Williams Wynn was always welcoming. Wynnstay itself had been recently rebuilt, to the design of James Wyatt. Its wide face with pillars and imposing portico dominated the shallow valley near Ruabon: a wall of local stone surrounded it like a necklace. It boasted the newly-fashionable black-and-white tiles on the wide floor of the entrance-hall, inside the tall double-doors. It was approached by a drive floored with pale sandstone which came up directly from the road a mile or so from Ruabon. Turning in from the road, beside the gatehouse and through the tall ornate gates wrought by the famous local Davies brothers, William looked forward to the splendid displays and especially the theatricals in the Wynnstay Theatre, which was three-roofed, custom-built, with interior decoration by Sandby, William Parry and other guests. In 1770 Sir Watkin had established an annual Theatre Season which was very popular. A particular favourite of William's in the painting-rich Wynnstay was a portrait which hung in the Stone Parlour, Meng's portrait of Richard Wilson: he was fascinated by the subject's commitment to his art and the look of exasperation as he is interrupted at his work.

Wynnstay set the standard, but few could emulate it. Its wealth was such that in the first half of the eighteenth century 'The Great Sir Watkin' (father of his present host) boasted a rental income of over £15,000 a year. All around him, William could see evidence of this. At dinner, servants swanned about them in unnecessary multiples.

Music was much in the style of the household. Each evening a different player, group and singer would entertain them in the drawing room, and when pressed William would stand alongside his brother Joseph and sing a duet or two in a very agreeable manner.

Property — they spoke of it regularly, looking around as

they sat enjoying their wine. Investment in land and property was fashionable and profitable. The improvement of an estate was a matter of the liveliest interest. In William's case, it was the acquisition of an estate, albeit a small one, that was of primary interest.

His brother John decided to build himself a house in Erith, east London. Below it, alongside the Thames, was an area of land, reclaimed in Elizabethan times. This was now cultivated and grew corn. His brother's house was not a large Hall but a house of pleasing proportions: ' a neat and elegant box,' as one correspondent observed.

On the 1st of February 1793, war was declared. John Madocks urged his son, now down from Oxford, to study for the Bar. So William settled into his father's chambers at Lincoln's Inn.

His father died the following year and was buried in the family vault at Gresford.

William became restless. His natural urge for activity came into conflict with work at the Law. As a child he had missed his old home Fron Yw in the Vale of Clwyd (where he now owned a few holdings bringing in rent of some £200 a year). Now the tug of Wales was on him again. He bought the Dolmelynllyn estate with his inherited money, but when he tired of that, the Glaslyn and Dwyryd increasingly occupied his mind.

The first time he saw *Tan-yr-Allt* properly, after he had bought the estate on which it sat, he knew he could do something with it. It was set high, but not too high. Rather like Fron Yw, with the valley below. It backed up to cliffs, but they did not overpower the rectangular stone farmhouse. In front of it was a wild plot which he could turn to grass, with flowers and shrubs. He would turn the house around. It was now set against the open space of the estuary with only two windows downstairs and two windows upstairs, with its front door on the cliff side. He would turn the front into an elegant face, with a veranda punctuated by trellis pillars across the entire lower storey, a local slate floor to the portico and an oak front door. The veranda was to have a slate roof which was to extend around the left and right front corners of the main building. The roof, originally pitched steep, would be rebuilt into a flatter shape with overhanging eaves. Windows were to be casement, not sash. In the living-room, the chimney-piece was to have narrow windows each side. Light, and the extensive view, was to be let into the house as a valued guest. The general effect of the house in his mind had a lightness about it, its overhanging eaves slanting outward rather like the sails of a beautiful boat. It would be 'a neat and elegant box' but a little more than that. It would be artistic.

And so it was to be. A young man, with luck on his side (and an inheritance) began to live his dream.

William quickly discovered who the best workers were. The main builder was from Criccieth; his yard was just below the castle. This Welshman got on well with the new incoming landowner. Money was to be made. His men worked hard, stripping the roof first, replacing the worn timbers, re-setting it, covering it with local Ffestiniog slate. There was much hitting and hammering as new windows were set in the stout walls, and William, visiting every month or so, was well pleased with progress. He was impressed by how intelligent the contractor was, and his workers. When they heard his instructions, they carried them out without further questions or time wasted. Rowlands, the contractor, saw the work nearly every day, in his dark waistcoat and polished black boots. He came with wages on Fridays, in brown envelopes.

What to do with the land thereabouts that he had bought as the Tan-y-Bwlch Estate was always on William's mind. Architecture and house improvement was one thing, and it was going well, but landscaping ('improvement') was something else.

One day, as he stood before his new house, looking over the water, he saw what was left of an embankment, some one hundred yards off shore in the Beddgelert direction. The land adjacent to this, he now owned. But this embankment had not been a success. It was now merely a line through the water and it tapered to an end. The idea had been a good one, reflected William, but the manpower, finance and quality of management to see it through had been missing. If that embankment had been finished, and it held, then all the land it enclosed would be his. And the estate would have cost him a great deal more. This would have increased his landholding by say nearly half of what he owned now. If he could expand his Tan-yr-Allt estate it would be something he could talk about with his landowning friends. The idea of improving and extending the embankment, or creating a new one on the sea side, thus claiming more land from the sea for himself, was attracting him.

The idea of a new town was also forming in his mind. Newly-built and planned. Not a higgledy-piggledy collection of cottages, as so many villages were in the country, but a properly planned town, with a central square, town hall, hotel, well-built stone houses, mostly in terraces, and tradespeople: cobbler, tailor, baker and so on. And of course a blacksmith so that horses were well shod. It was to be a borough; elegant in appearance and self-sustaining in economy as much as possible. He imagined conversations in the street, people from all walks of life, from the local lawyer to the local gravedigger getting on well, all contributing to the communal effort and happiness. William kept it mostly to himself because he realised that parts of this idea brought him into conflict with the *status quo,* the landowning classes, who saw people largely as beings to be used, exploited, to the greater glory and wealth of the educated, endowed, privileged classes. To them, the *elite,* a happy society was a stable society, where people knew their place, under the benevolent control of their betters. To William, a happy society was a place where brotherhood prevailed, where people of all persuasions lived in mutual tolerance, respect and harmony, each contributing in his own way to the general good.

If he could rescue this corner of the landscape, below his feet to the right, from the sea, he could build his new town here. In the centre would be a cross of streets; its back against the cliffs, its wings — the far way to Caernarfon, this way to Betws-y-Coed and Shrewsbury — the central stem heading for Ynys-y-Towyn.

Behind him, this summer's day, the carpenter and roofer were finishing the roof of the veranda. Rhododendrons in shades of blue were blooming on the slope overlooking the sea.

A young man was bending towards the ground under the overhang, laying slate slabs on the portico floor. He dipped his trowel into the bucket of cement, wiping the edges so as not to drop any. He laid the irregular pavings to make an exact fit, raising and levelling off the underneath with granite chippings. He checked their flatness by the use of a long, end-tapered spirit-level. Then he grouted the laid stones with a softer cement, checking again with the spirit-level and sometimes tapping with a wooden mallet. A wet cloth over the grouting finished the job. William turned to watch him. He was barely sixteen. He wore a clean blue dotted handkerchief around his neck, brown trousers with creases under his cotton builders' apron and when he was handling slate he pulled on a pair of thin leather gloves. Something in his appearance, clothing and application to his work: methodical, painstaking, time-saving appealed to William. He went over to talk with him.

"Good afternoon," he started, politely but pointedly.

The man looked up. He did not have the face of an artisan; it was not weathered but pale.

"Sir?" he replied tentatively.

"You work for Mister Rowlands, the builder?" William questioned.

"I am learning," he replied. "I do parts in turn. Timber, windows, plaster. I need to do some plumbing soon. I trained as a gardener in Plas Newydd, but I decided to move on and learn the building trade."

His sense of order, his desire to learn, his apparent reliability and his command of English all impressed William, as he stood there alone against the backdrop of his life's work.

Suddenly, and without really thinking about it, William acted on a whim which was to be one of the luckiest gestures of his life, "And would you work for me?"

The young man looked him full in the eyes. He paused. He said, "I will."

"Your name?" said William.

"John Williams. Of Anglesey. Sir."

They stood side-by-side. Beneath them was the site for the new town. And beneath them was the blue lake of Traeth Mawr. On the other side of the estuary was Ffestiniog with its huge reserves of slate.

Below them was the theatre of William's ambition, his stage. He had great work to do. His imagination had focused on this corner of Eifionnydd and he was eager to apply his ideas.

But he could not do this on his own. He needed somebody who could act out his ambitions, who understood his imagination. Somebody who was quick to understand and wasted no time in carrying ideas into action, project to result. He had to be a Welsh-speaker.

"Speak Welsh?" he enquired.

"Of course. Perfectly. Brought up near Llangefni," he replied.

Together they could be as the left hand and the right hand

of a body. Together they could achieve what no man could achieve alone.

This youth (he looked at him again and felt it again) was the man for the job.

William put out his hand. John took it. Their hands moved in unison, up and down, as behind them the seawater and the pure water of the Glaslyn pumped, eddied and swung as the energies collided and unified.

Chapter 5

Clearly, the embankment was crucial to the plan. It would have to be built long and secure. Its length was daunting. But if the sea was to be kept back and land around two sides of the estuary adjoining the Tan-yr-Allt Estate was to be reclaimed, it would need to be some two miles long.

William Madocks consulted a man called James Creassy who had experience of such schemes, especially in Lincolnshire. Standing before Tan-yr-Allt, there was much pointing and arm movement by the two men. Creassy had the confidence of a man who had seen it all before. He insisted on the quality and sturdiness of the sluices and on digging out the bottom parts of the hill streams so that water flowed swiftly to the sea and did not stay to turn the reclaimed land into marsh.

William and John considered using the present embankment as part of it, perhaps adding some three feet in height. But the more they thought of that, the less they liked it. The old embankment was too close to shore. If a job is to be done, it better be done properly. They were going to build a new embankment set about two hundred yards on the seawards side of the old one and then curve it round well away from Pen Morfa, leaving enough room for the new village of Tremadog, and then bring it more or less straight towards the footings of Moel-y-Gest at Ynys-y-Towyn. It was an ambitious project. Its height was estimated at twenty feet maximum, thirteen feet minimum. The winter of 1799–1800 was, fortunately, a mild one, following a summer which was wet and windy. This had affected the cereal harvest and farmers were in poverty. It was a good time to hire labour.

So John Williams, a boy among men, set to work. Born in

1778, he was bred on a small farm called Ty'n Llan at Llanfihangel Ysgeifiog in the south of Anglesey, where the land, overlooking Afon Cefni and Malltraeth Marsh, was thin and infertile. He and his brothers knew that the place would not support them so he left home at the age of thirteen. He knew what it was to scrape for a living. He had seen his father and mother do it, his father's face getting whiter and more strained before he died at the age of fifty-two.

He took over the hiring. He was looking to employ men who were used to hard work. Farmers, small-holding men like himself, were best; they were used to getting up early and working a long day. They were used to bending the back, digging with a spade, heaving the sand, pushing wheelbarrows obliquely up the slope. Their numbers grew as demand increased, and the necessary sluices, with their secure foundations and oak-frameworks, took up much time and specialist manpower. But mostly it was a hard slog, digging, transporting. A trickle of Irishmen appeared, worked hard, and more followed them.

His relationship with his employer, William Madocks, was an odd one. John knew that they were very different people. Madocks was a social person; he loved conviviality, dinners, week-ends with interesting companions. He kept Tan-yr-Allt as a new lively household, oil lamps in the windows and the flash of carriage lamps as they swerved to turn around alongside the house. William kept in touch, certainly, but it was little more than that. He strode down regularly from his house to chat with John and inspect progress on this first embankment: he had quickly learned that he could put his faith in John Williams. Partly as a management strategy, partly out of insouciance, he left the running of the new enterprise to his trusty lieutenant. He put cash in his hand and left the rest to him. William loved to chat with his week-end guests at Tan-yr-Allt, waving his arm down towards the new embankment, briefly explaining the grand idea and saying casually, "The work is proceeding well."

John was up at dawn. He knew the tides. At the first moment of the sea's ebb, he had his men working. He had selected them for their physique and work-rate; they were strong, with big shoulders, arms and hands. This is where he learned the importance of selecting the right men and motivating them to work As they sat at 10:30am, taking their tea, pouring it into the cupped lids of their tins, they reflected on the vigour and determination of this young man. At twelve they would break for a short dinner, mostly of oatmeal and *llymru*, a porridge-like substance which was very nutritious. As the cold of early evening came on, they would gather brushwood and ignite it, sitting, holding out their hands, singing their favourite Welsh songs. *Dafydd y Garreg Wen* was a great favourite; its origin, as they all knew, only some two miles distant on the farm Garreg Wen, at Morfa Bychan, where the harpist played his requiem: the 'white rock' itself sat on a field at Borth-y-Gest, above the small bay behind the distant headland.

One evening, William Madocks, coming down to the traeth, heard the men sing, and he was reminded of his visit to the shoreline of northern Spain, to the west of Santander, where in a small village, in the warm dusk, he heard a group of fishermen sing their native songs. In both situations, the voices were in harmony, controlled and even, the consonants strong, the pitch secure. He formed the idea that there was something of the Spanish in these people.

John Williams' Welsh was better than that of the men who worked for him. He knew more words, a tribute to his study of a Welsh dictionary on his family's Anglesey farm. He had been a book-learner at his home and school in Llangefni. By speaking to his men in Welsh, he entered their minds. They would not be working as hard as this for an Englishman; they would have been taking his money and going home as soon as possible. But this was a task to be proud of. They were making their homeland. They would beat the sea back. As their hands held their spades, a sense of determination entered them and the earth flew as it was removed. The embankment, built of hand-removed sand, earth and turf, grew almost as if it was a living thing. It snaked across Traeth Mawr for some two miles, secured at the Caernarfonshire side to the lower reaches of Moel-y-Gest, and at the Meirionnydd end it attached itself against rocks where the Glaslyn appeared out of its narrow valley.

One morning, at six, John inspected progress. Water had come three feet up the mound, but no more. He thought they were about right in their calculations. Then he asked the men if they knew reliable men to help them because he proposed to start building at the other end. He had made the calculation that if they were to build from one end only, it would get very difficult towards the other end. He'd rather finish the job in the middle. Forty men came forward, some being the sons of the ones already there, who now, their hands calloused and their backs stiff, advised on the best technique of digging, throwing and patting-down. Horses and carts carried the sandy soil, grass was cut and laid over the mound and by the end of March, the end of the project was in sight. It had been a remarkable effort, impossible but for the leadership of the young man, who had thickened-out as he grew his final inches, but always his calm manner, precise instructions and leadership, amounting to inspiration, carried the day.

But with most of the work completed and a sense of accomplishment beginning to spread through the men, one night punctuated what had otherwise been a lucky job. John lay in his bed in his rented room. The wind rose to a howl, his window shaking. He listened again and the wind howled again. This corresponded with a high tide. He looked at his watch; it was nine-thirty-one. He dressed, put on his long coat, collected a shovel and headed for the embankment. The water was higher than ever before. He stood with his back to Tan-yr-Allt as the water slapped the other side of the mound. He dug in a row, cleanly cutting the sod, raising and throwing, until a line of new earth ran across the top of the embankment. He worked at the crucial area which was about twenty feet long. Then he went back and dug another row, throwing the earth higher. He did this for over two hours, working quickly. The moon in its fullness reappeared, the wind abated and stars appeared. William knew he had done enough to avert a disaster. He was wet through, covered in earth, mud and grass. He walked back to his lodgings knowing that it had been a close thing.

The next morning, in the new daylight, the men faced the embankment and saw a fresh layer of earth lying across the top. William said nothing as he came to work at 6:20. The men quickly covered the new section with fresh soil and clods of grass, trampling it down.

The following day, William sat down to write to his lady-friend. He wrote, 'Dear Coz, I am now at Penmorva amidst 150 wheelbarrowers and 200 spades — and hearts too — all attempting Canute-like to set boundaries to the Ocean and make old Neptune back his chariot . . . I am now sitting in a Fisherman's hut on the Seashore and am fancying I have learned that *Man wants little here below.*'

His flowery turn of phrase contrasted with the incisive manner and work ethic of the young man who was pushing his schemes forward.

Chapter 6

A local rector, three months after the completion of the embankment, wrote in a letter to a friend: 'I can also assert that the finest clover I ever beheld grew where there were only sands, prior to this great undertaking.' Over a thousand acres had been reclaimed. In the first year it was laid to oats and in the following two years, wheat, rape and barley, then grass seeds.

And William Thomas, looking down at Traeth Mawr from Ysgubor Goch, was equally praising and confident: *"Mae'r gwaith wedi gorffen; y werddglof yn dal a'r glaswerth yn tyfu."* This acknowledged that the work was finished, the embankment was holding and new grass was growing.

The first improvement was to transport. The road around the shoreline towards Beddgelert was now not subject to regular flooding. It had been re-surfaced and a horse and carriage could traverse it regularly, independent of the rising tide. This was of special benefit to those who lived on Lleyn, who wanted to take the southern route to England. It also fitted-in with Madocks' idea that traffic to Ireland would come this way. The small inlet at Porthdinllaen, on the north coast of Lleyn, a deep water port, was being eyed as an ideal sailing setting-off point to Ireland, given some improvements.

Pen Morfa ('The head of the sea-shore') no longer lived up to its name. The blue lake of Traeth Mawr had lost its extremities. It was now restricted by the new embankment and Pen Morfa found itself some two miles distant from the waters of Cardigan Bay when in full tide. Madocks' dream of a new borough, a designed and properly inhabited new town was now a possibility, built on land newly claimed.

William wrote to his mother: 'You must promise to spend a month with me in Snowdonia in the autumn. You have not half a notion of the chaos till you have explored these mountains. Cader Idris is a polished place of some of the lofty and rugged scenery I can show you. I am grown a great sailor and Cardigan Bay on a fine day is the rehearsal of Elysium. How should you like to play with a Solar Microscope? There is such an abundance of natural curiosities, particularly marine about these coasts . . . I think we might venture to enlist one for next summer. The insects, fish and transparent vegetables are here beautiful and rare.'

In view of the possibility of a visit by his mother, William, with his faithful builder, set to improve Tan-yr-Allt and when finished it boasted two ground-floor parlours, a stair hall in the middle and three bedrooms above. He was proud of coverage in the European Magazine: 'Mr Madocks' cottage . . . was built more for a convenient residence than for splendour of show.' Its large roofing slates, brought from Penrhyn Quarry, Bethesda, were a local talking-point. One parlour was lined with silk; most of the chimney-pieces were made of local slate, with one of marble, shipped from London. The wall looking over what was to be the new town of Tremadog was supplied with two windows over the fireplace and in the bedroom above a window was set immediately above the fireplace, the flue bent around it. An old pantry was converted to a lavatory with water closet; William was particularly pleased with this, very much an innovation in this neck of the woods. William wanted a lovely garden, so that scents and petals would blow through the french window into the parlour. He wrote: 'Mignonette & Sweet Peas, universally & in abundance . . . and roses [he wrote the number 1,000]' The walled garden was well-stocked with peas, beans, broccoli, lettuce, chervil and chicory. Raspberry and strawberry were favourites. Huw, the gardener, worked diligently to his master's instructions, and when house-parties arrived, the garden supplied them with fresh produce.

All this planning and activity, both on the base of the bay and in and around Tan-yr-Allt, contrasted with the sparse, utilitarian, lives of even the better-off of the area's farmers. William Thomas of Ysgubor Goch with his faithful, hard-working wife Margaret continued their improvements to their farm. They built a new milking-parlour and their milk had a reputation for purity and quantity of cream. Richard was growing into a boy of energy and brains. He had built by hand the iron baskets that kept the hay fresh for the cows at milking. He made a gate which swung perfectly on its hinges, so that the Minister was impressed when he came to visit.

"A boy of much quality," he said in English, "he is going to take us somewhere."

Richard received the compliment with a short smile and a nod of his head.

"He makes things," said his mother. "He is not afraid of fire. He can make a new gate out of a pile of old iron."

"One day, he will lead the way. We have to move forward, Mrs Thomas," the Minister reflected.

Richard proved his application and originality when, one windy morning, their horse Maggie was missing. She was not a mare of great work but she had produced three foals of quality, with strong shoulders and safe feet. They searched for her and found her lying on her side in the far field, in the teeth of the wind. It was obvious that she was injured in the leg. Closer examination revealed a foot out-of-line. She had probably turned to protect herself from the wind and caught her foot on one of the stones that lay strongly anchored in the earth.

"Mag bach," said William as he stroked her back. He knew she was a good breeder and mother and could be again; but her life as puller of plough and cart had probably come to an end.

"Perhaps I can do something," said Richard in Welsh, stepping forward to examine the injured leg. "Perhaps a kind of splint."

He accompanied his father and Maggie, limping and dragging her foot, back to the warmest of the farm buildings. And soon Richard was at work, shaping iron. He had his fire burning strongly, and his beating of iron could be heard as far as the road. He created four ribs, indented on the inside, with double slits resembling button-holes. He created four belts of strong leather. He connected the ends of the iron frame with leather, rolling it over the ends, using sheep's wool as padding. He attached brass buckles on the leather belts. He threaded the belts through the slits in the four ribs. Early one morning, well after the wind had abated and a fine silver light lay on the hillside, he approached the stone byre where the mare stood in some pain, her lower leg raised. He patted her, spoke with her and she looked at him with apprehension. He reached for the leg, raised it slowly, protecting the broken section. Carefully he wrapped on the splint. He drew at the belts, fastening the buckles tight but not too tight. It fitted and it looked as if it would work. His eye had been very good; its size exactly right and its system of adjustment suited to the leg's uneven thickness. Maggie put her leg down slowly. She seemed to know that some good had been done to her. As Richard left the byre with his tools in a broad wooden tray, the mare looked at him and raised her ears.

It had been a triumph. Two weeks later, after the best oats and plenty of fresh water, Mag was back on the fields. She was never to drag heavy weights again, but she went on to produce more fine foals.

This event attached itself to Richard and never went away. He quickly developed a reputation as a master of iron. Neighbours came in their carts with their damaged axles and a day later called again to collect the repaired piece. Very large, or small, Richard could fix it, and create something new. Some of his designs were original, owing little to previous traditional methods. One of his favourites was repairing and changing the weakened front springs on carts and carriages, when the driver's seat would bump and sway. When he had finished with its support system, the seat sat square, and when descending a hill or turning a sharp corner, it kept its occupant erect and safe.

Chapter 7

"John," said William Madocks, as they walked side-by-side down the drive of Tan-yr-Allt, "I have been made an offer."

"Sir," he replied, "what is that?"

"I have been accepted as a prospective Member of Parliament."

This was quite a shock to John, who thought that his employer had so attached himself to this area that he would seldom have need to leave, apart from visits to London, to Dolmelynllyn and the houses of his brothers.

"For where, Sir?" asked John, expecting a reference to an area not far away; Cheshire, for instance.

"Boston, Lincolnshire," he replied.

John was shocked. All that huge distance between here and there. That was on the other side of England.

"A very long way away," he said, trying to seem calm.

"But we can manage, can't we?" said William, laying his hand on John's arm.

"We probably can," said John, "but what about the plans, for the town," he said, waving his arm towards the projected site of their town.

"We shall build it," was the sturdy response. "You will be my agent. You will be the mind behind the project. And I know you will succeed." This confidence in him deeply moved John Williams, son of an impoverished Anglesey farmer.

"We will succeed," he replied, not wanting to seem alone in this. He knew he could do the on-the-ground work, the careful planning, the Welsh speaking, the organising of labour, but in the end he was a doer rather than a thinker. Madocks had vision. He had not. Madocks had enthusiasm, and finance. But he, John Williams, was faithful. He would carry out his master's wishes. Loyalty was in his bones.

Standing for Parliament was an expensive business. Votes had to be bought and people entertained. But the project succeeded and William Madocks could put MP after his name. His mother was proud, but concerned. Her eldest son was ambitious and needed help. She considered her assets and advanced over eight thousand pounds to William against his part in her will. But Frances Madocks had not long to live. She died in Margate in 1804. The family home, Mount Mascall, came to him in trust with another man, who died shortly thereafter, and William sold it to his brother.

Porthdinllaen, on the north coast of Lleyn, was growing as a port en-route for travellers to Ireland, and the present route to Ireland was fraught with danger; Snowdonia needed to be negotiated, the crossing to Anglesey across theStraits was hazardous even at the lowest tide and the step across the water to Holy Island and Holyhead equally dangerous.

The crossing of Traeth Mawr with a new road on an embankment was not a new idea. It had been mooted by Sir John Wynn of Gwydir in the early seventeenth century. He approached Sir Hugh Myddelton who had made his name by designing and having constructed a long canal to bring fresh water to London. He wrote to Sir John from his house on St Peter's Square, Ruthin, thanking him for his interest, quietly rejecting the '. . . few hundred pounds . . .' promised and saying, with considerable foresight, that the area did not have the 'great stones' which would be needed for an embankment and that the cost would run in to thousands, not hundreds, of pounds.

Ireland had become part of Great Britain and travelling to and fro increased. From Dublin to London was a long and tedious journey. Travelling via Porthdinllaen meant that travellers would step on to Madocks' property. They would need food and shelter, overnight accommodation and stabling for the horses. They would need a shop to buy goods for the journey on to London via Chester or Shrewsbury or Ludlow. And a blacksmith to shoe the horses.

Chapter 8

The correspondence began in earnest. Quarto sheets with spidery writing in sepia. William dashed them off to John as he felt fit. They had no formality, often no address and date. They came as if they were spoken, part of the conversation between the two men which was conducted over a hundred miles of distance. John kept the letters; he opened them with a letter-knife and after reading, placed them in a neat pile in a wooden tray. This, when full, was emptied and the letters placed in a box sitting on the floor. Sometimes John wrote the date, in his careful round hand, at the head of the leaf. Sometimes they went on and on, many pages covered by this pigs' tail of a script, sometimes with drawings of architectural details, poorly drawn, for Madocks was no trained architect. But he did have an eye for space and symmetry, and this is what Tremadog embodied in its plan.

The idea of the town was in his head, and he had convinced himself that economically and socially it was viable. He was thinking of creating a business, an industry, for the employment of locals and their children. Something to do with fabric, cotton or wool, he thought, noting the quantity of sheep which grazed the Caernarfonshire hills, and the need of the army for uniforms and tents.

Not without self-knowledge or trepidation, however, Madocks wrote one letter to John at 'Tan-y-Rallt, Carnarvon,' which finished: 'Wishing us both good luck, I remain Your sincere friend W. A. Madocks.'

Luck, it seemed, was needed in spades-full. How to plan a town? He wanted it organic; he wanted people intermingling and creating their own energy in the way they went about things. Buying and selling, cooking, having conversations, giving advantages to their children, it would all need to knit together. But happiness to the eye was important; you had to enjoy being where you were. It was no good waking up each morning and seeing only bricks, stones and a glimpse of sky; such a life was belittling to the spirit. There would need to be beauty in the setting, harmony in the design.

He was working it out. London Street, on the Ynys Towyn side, was to be presented in dressed stone and slate, no thatch. There was, to the visitor, to be a chapel and a church seen first, and in the borough a hotel and coach-house to accommodate travellers, two inns for the locals, one shop and, for constructive work, a fulling mill for cleaning and thickening cloth, a corn mill for the production of flour and a tannery for the creation of leather. It was all hugely ambitious. It needed time, dedication, a steady stream of finance and management. He was convinced that John could handle it.

"It will happen," said Madocks as the two men walked side-by-side, their backs to Cardigan Bay and before them, the tall rocks. "That rock," said Madocks as he raised his hand, "will be the background and centre, as the prow of a ship."

Later, at his London house, Madocks penned a sketch showing the central layout. He had marked houses for Griffiths, Jones, Humphreys, who were the builders in charge, and a Mayor's House. He indicated that a flagpole was to be erected below the great crag. He wrote: 'I am paying heavily every week for Carpenters at the Town, and can not find anything done. I have been absent from home nearly 2 months & Robert Jones' Cottage is not even roofed . . . What have the town carpenters been about? . . . Now do, once for all, attend to this immediately and effectually . . ."

He did not, of course, appreciate the difficulties. He had left a young man to organise it all, to find capable carpenters (ones who knew about joists, jambs, window frames and the like rather than wheelwrighting and shaft-shaping), creators of proper foundations for housing (mostly terraced), stone masons, slaters for roofs, and so on. The task was prodigious.

His letters continued their cajoling, 'Drive on the New Inn . . . Is the Mayor's house begun? . . . Drive Griffith on with houses and Steeple to the Church. I must have the Steeple done soon . . . When I know jobs are going on spiritedly I do not mind the money."

Small firms had been contracted to build different parts of the town. The Town Hall was a focus-point and Madocks was very keen for it to be completed soon: "Drive on the Town, & Mill etc. for Griffiths having so many hands ready, he can knock off the Mill and 5 or 6 New houses at the Market, beside finishing Dr Morris's house. I wish you would agree with him to finish the Mill and 6 houses by the 1st of July . . . and make the best bargain you can with John Griffiths, whose workmen and timber are so handy . . . If Griffiths is likely to be dearer than Humphrey on the same plan, or Humphrey may grumble but I trust 100 guineas a house will be a full [?] price. I leave this entirely to your judgement . . .' The Market Place was not entirely planned and John Williams was left to make 'trifling alterations' to the design. Such was the responsibility and trust laid upon him by Madocks, resident of London and MP for Boston, Lincolnshire.

Chapter 9

Work was going on below Ysgubor Goch at high speed. Smoke rose, white dust punctuated the lower air, hammering continued from early morning to dusk, carts, large and small, travelled the road through their land, and in the byre and other farm buildings, iron pieces, implements, ploughs repaired and needing repairs, spread all over the ground floor and hung on the walls. Richard's ironwork business was booming.

"Cer i siarad efo'r dyn," said his father one day, in some exasperation at the ironwork spreading over his property. *"A gofyn iddo am le."* This told his son to go and talk with John Williams and ask him for a workplace, a smithy.

He caught the young man in the corner of the Market Square, looking up at joists being laid.

He addressed him in Welsh — "Good Morning, Mister Williams. I am Richard Williams of Ysgubor Goch."

By now he was getting used to his new name. His last name was his father's first name. The regulations on names had been changed.

"Of course," replied John, lowering his eyes and looking at the farmer intently, "I know of your work. I have been thinking of approaching you but things have not yet got really bad here in iron. We are managing to make simple things such as handles and gates . . ." So his reputation had preceded him.

"I am looking for a new place to work. My business in iron is expanding. I think I can make a living out of it."

"Shoe horses?" said John, typically concentrating on the most needy and immediate.

"Of course," said Richard, "have been shoeing horses since I was five."

"Come this way," said John. He put his arm on Richard's shoulder and guided him around the corner into the Caernarfon Road. He pointed to his left.

"A yard," he said. "Direct access from the main road. Three-sided. Open at this side, plenty of access space. Four guineas a month."

That the rental came so quickly after the description of the building not yet created was typical of the man.

"I'll take it," said Richard, realising that this was a good site. It was at the end of the town where tired, possibly damaged, horses and carts would enter after the journey across the thinly inhabited stretch from Pwllheli and Caernarfon; horses would need shoeing, wheels re-ironed and so on. Much potential business.

"Here's a sovereign as deposit." He pressed the gold coin into John's hand, who then reached a pocket-book from his coat pocket, wrote down the transaction with a pencil, returning the red-bound book to his pocket.

"Come back in a month and the building will be ready," said John with his usual confidence.

He walked back.

"Da iawn, fy mab i," said his father. Well done, my boy.

And so, a tradition was started.

Richard became the tradesman in iron at the new town. He was the first specialist artisan to occupy a premises there. Soon his building was a working smithy and much more. It was festooned with bits and pieces — rusty, hooked, polished, pointed, broken and repaired. There was nothing that Richard could not do in metal. Sometimes a job puzzled him but he would go home up the hill, think about it in the evening and after starting work at six-thirty, when his silver and russet fire with its leaping flames in the open chimney was ready for work, by eight o'clock he had usually solved the problem and put the piece up against the wall to cool and be collected.

Chapter 10

Madocks knew what great architecture was. His time in London as a boy and youth in Charterhouse had presented him with sightings of buildings which lifted the heart and mind. Sir Christopher Wren's great churches were like great paintings, challenging, original, messages in aesthetic, often glimpsed down a narrow street, or presenting themselves on the pavement with a grace and elegance that was often in great contrast to nearby buildings, which looked leaden and ugly. His buildings had the lightness of flight; they had a reaching skywards of the finest, best-trimmed, trees. They had the pulse of life about them; they were human, spiritual and beautiful. And inside, their spaces were as the curvature of a shell, the sound within echoing the flow and rush of blood in the body.

Great architecture was that which enhanced life. It took the best of people, set it in its rightful place, allowed it to move, gesticulate, talk. It was a setting for life, as a jewel is enhanced by the embrace of gold and silver.

He had been a reader of books of architectural design. A landscape improver, he and his friends were fascinated by European trends: Florence was of particular interest. Late mediaeval building design here had that scale and beauty which contrasted sharply with the ponderous scale and detailing of the English country house. Street scenes in Florence merged utility with pleasantness so that its inhabitants drew a certain confidence from their environment. The Piazza Santissima Annunziata, designed by the great Florentine architect Brunelleschi, had a special appeal: it was a space for enjoyment, work and healing, reflecting the human. Its loggias were built on platforms above ground level, accessible up a flight of steps. Columns were spaced evenly apart, their height slightly smaller than the width between them. The over-riding arch formed a hemisphere, set over a cube. Between the arches were roundels incorporating a design. As you stood in the square, the regular columns surrounded you and the buildings behind were easily accessible: it was all in human scale, uplifting to the spirit.

He would build a church and a chapel. The church was to be the first Gothic revival church in Wales. The chapel was to be striking, based on Inigo Jones' Covent Garden chapel in London.

The new borough would have a beautiful heart, the Market Square. The square would have terraced stone houses around it. Its focus would be the Town Hall, set directly below the dramatic cliff, its front at a right-angle to London Street. Important visitors would come in via this street and be greeted by symmetry and order, the tall rock in the centre, the Town Hall centred below with its five arches, all raised off the ground with the terrace of cottages along High Street, stretching to the south, with steps up to their front doors to give them height and protection from flooding. The Prince of Wales Inn, later the Madocks Arms, on the other side of the Town Hall, would signify welcome with good fare and accommodation.

The Town Hall would have an open lower level, copying the Florentine loggia or arcade. It would rise four steps up from ground level. Its façade would have five Florentine arches, each one separated by a roundel with an image of a leaf and flower. The open space inside would be slate-floored and could be used by citizens for many purposes, possibly as a market, possibly as a meeting-place. Above it on the first floor was to be the Hall or Dancing Room; the entrance to this space was through the hotel next-door. This would allow ladies and gentlemen, attendees at a play or musical event, to leave their over-coats, and not have to pass through the market hall below; and it would give the entertainers a place to change into their theatrical clothes. The back wall featured a musicians' gallery and the stage was set next to the adjacent house on High Street. Madocks was excited by theatre. He loved events, plays, parties, special occasions: he also loved, and here embodied, in this new town which he created with his own hand, the theatre of good architecture.

Chapter 11

Elinor lay on her back in bed, heavily pregnant. Richard was very attentive, bringing her food and drink when he was not sweating away at his trade in iron in the new smithy. He was in his element, seeing people, fixing their broken items, chatting, hammering, handing over the repaired piece with a smile.

She looked through the window, seeing the shoulder of Moel-y-Gest spattered with sheep.

"*Elinor,*" came a voice from downstairs, "*wyt ti'n iawn?*"

She replied with a cheery affirmative. Her mother-in-law was very kind. Despite her increasing age, she was vigorous and positive. Outside the window Elinor heard the cries of chickens and geese and further away, the wobbly cries of lambs. A goose was a family mealtime favourite. Every excuse was found for a feast; William cracking his carving knife against the sharpener, eyeing the breast-bone, slicing downwards with precision.

"What shall we call the new baby?" said Elinor, as Richard sank into his chair.

"Boy or girl?" he replied.

"Let's say it is a boy," she said. "I think it should be William."

Richard thought this a suitable compliment to his father, who had brought so much into their lives.

"And Margaret if it is a girl?" asked Richard tentatively.

"Of course," replied Elinor. "That will be very good."

It was in the early morning when Richard was woken by a kick to his groin.

"*Yn dod,*" said Elinor. This said that the baby was coming. He quickly got dressed, told his parents his intention, saddled young Jimmy, their fastest and fittest horse and set off, for the midwife. He had been there before, on a trial run for this occasion, for he was not one to leave things to chance. The village of Garndolbenmaen, with its ancient church and tall trees, was awakening as he clattered in. It was the end house of the terrace. He raised the iron knocker and tried to slam it down without too much noise. She came to the door, her head-dress from the night still on her head. He explained the circumstances. She looked at him with pleasure, stroking her left arm. *"Da iawn, fy 'ngwas i."* She was congratulating him. The area needed new blood, and she loved the task of bringing children into the world. She finished her dressing, went outside to the stables, and soon both her ample-size white mare and Richard's young stallion were making their even way back to Penmorfa as the sun made its final preparations for lighting the day.

"Bachgen," yelled Richard, *"Dad, un ar dy ol di."* He was telling his father that the newcomer was to be named after him. William Thomas stood at the fireplace and took down the bottle he had been saving. Carefully, he placed four glasses on the table. With his wife Margaret beside him, his son and the midwife before him he poured the whiskey, raised his glass, saying, "Another man. Another man of iron. Let him start his own fire and prosper. Let him turn the poor and broken into the working, flourishing and fertile." This was said in Welsh, in rhetoric the equal of any language.

After the child had emptied its lungs and throat of noise, he settled down to sleep. The midwife brought him down to the kitchen in a wicker basket. "And there he is," she said with a broad smile, "a lovely boy." He possessed thick black hair, high cheek-bones, a strong chin and a look of determination.

The following day, Richard's smithy was a hive of activity and talk. An event such as the birth of a first son was not to be kept quiet. Soon all his neighbours along Dublin

Street and across the market square knew. They came in to shake his hand and all day he worked with his friends and neighbours in attendance, all delighted at his good fortune.

John Williams came: "Very pleased, Richard. A first son. Congratulations." He shook his hand warmly. "This is the first son of our new town. We shall treasure him. He will go on to great things. This year, eighteen hundred and six, is the birth-point, the turning-point."

As he said this, he looked over towards Penrhyn-deudraeth and the rocks of Penrhyn Isa, on the far side of the estuary. He imagined what Madocks was now telling him in instalments, in letters and in the occasional personal visit, that they would build the second embankment. That it would carry traffic to and from London. That their new town ('borough' said Madocks) would be the joining-place of movement of people and goods from Ireland, through Porthdinllaen as the new sea-port on the north coast of Lleyn, over the Glaslyn, through to Shrewsbury, Oxford and London. From the bleak, neglected place it was a few years ago, with an almost empty population, this corner of Caernarfonshire would change to a place of bustling life and prosperity.

'We need new people,' thought John Williams, 'people of quality and vision. This family, these Williamses, are the right stuff. They have brains, ambition, and a desire to work hard.'

Chapter 12

The clipper had a workmanlike aspect. Its two stout sails were used to high winds. It had sailed close to the shoreline, crossing the Aberdyfi Bar and the treacherous Dysynni shallows, passing by Barmouth with a familiar manner because she was built in Barmouth. All down the coast of Cardigan Bay and Tremadog Bay there was a tradition of boat-building. Men had gathered in sheltered coves and beaches, made a cradle, chamfered local oak into planks, heated them over coke fires to bend them to the right curved shape, plugged and bolted them together, heated pitch, slapping it into the gaps to create a water-tight vessel. Carpenters with their many skills finished the job on deck, making stout structures for crew and captain and plenty of room to store and make secure goods to be carried for profit.

These goods were usually stored in wooden packing-cases and John Williams could see them now, secured by ropes. Each case had the word 'Madocks' painted on it, so there was no doubting who owned this load and who it was hoped had paid for the carriage.

A stout man made his way between the boxes.

"Captain Sam Phillips," shouted John.

"Sir," came the reply, "at your service." He was a jolly man, and inclined to be a little theatrical.

"Good trip?" enquired John.

"Yes, Sir. Fine and dandy. My little ship is a trouper. Gets through in all weathers. Now, let's get this stuff on shore."

John had brought half-a-dozen men with him and with the boat's crew they soon had eight lines of packing-cases next to one another on the shore.

From his pocket John drew a sheaf of papers featuring the unmistakable Madocks handwriting.

"Two of these contain the gateway for our new church," he announced proudly, for two cases were larger than the others and much heavier.

He signed the bill of lading, took off his hat to the resolute Captain Phillips, his crew and his Barmouth-born boat. "God speed to you all," he pronounced as the clipper had its sails adjusted. It pulled away, heading for Caernarfon.

Chapter 13

In February 1807, Madocks had his Traeth Mawr Bill through Parliament. This gave him the right to build the new embankment across the mouth of the Glaslyn at his own expense. It gave him ownership of reclaimed land, although marshland rental was to bring him one-fifth of the income.

Madocks was feeling very pleased with himself. He had taken up the challenge of being a Member of Parliament for Boston, Lincolnshire, knowing that this would entail his absence from Caernarfonshire for long periods. He had his altruistic side. He was a Whig. He wanted reform. He wanted an end to the power of the landowners, to charge high rents and tithes, to manipulate voting, to create laws for their own advantage.

This dual nature of his life London/Boston in the south and east, and in a distant corner of the north-west, his new borough in Caernarfonshire, weighed on him, but he thought he could handle it. He had chosen well in John Williams. Every fortnight or so he sent a reliable man on a good horse to the north-west, carrying in a leather case a wad of notes; sometimes three hundred pounds, sometimes more. John acknowledged each consignment, setting it down in his own diaried ledger and also sending a receipt via the post office in Caernarfon. This money was as blood to the area. It went into workmen's pockets, allowing them to raise a family, feed and clothe their children. Via these wages, new businesses were born, shops started, inns created. House-builders employing carpenters, stone-masons, labourers, slaters started up, as did chandlers, sailmakers, tailors, lawyers. David Ellis (later Ellis-Nanney, Attorney-General for North Wales), first seen by Madocks as the man with grey eyebrows and a signet ring on his right hand in the Beddgelert inn, became a friend and colleague of Madocks' and put up money to erect a splendid house, Ty Nanney, on the edge of Tremadog, opposite the new church and close to the new chapel; a house with all the architectural qualities Madocks liked — the low-slung roof with overhanging eaves, bold lintels, casement windows, a trellis porch around the front door.

Religion, thought Madocks, is in the soul of a people. And these people have created a new route for themselves. They have rejected Anglicanism. They have turned to something more personal, more austere. He determined to build a chapel in Tremadog (the new name was beginning to enter his mind). It would be set apart. It would have a design unlike any other school or church, something to be proud of.

His favouring of the Calvinistic Methodists brought him into disfavour with the Bishop of Bangor. So he decided to balance things up by erecting a new church, again on its own ground, again in a significant location. It would be built on an outcrop of rock on the right as you entered the town. Services here would be principally in the English language, in contrast with the old churches at Penmorfa and Ynyscynhaearn, where services were in Welsh. He told his friends, in a wry aside, that he had placated the Bishop of Bangor by telling him that the chapel Peniel was built on sand whereas the new church was built on rock.

The church was to be in gothic style. It was built of brick covered in a plaster which gave the appearance of old stone. Its spire appeared taller than it really was because the church was built on a rocky outcrop. After its completion it was described: '. . . very beautiful. . .' with two fine pictures on each side of the altar piece, the one of the Woman taken in Adultery, & the other of the Tribute Money shewn to our Saviour, & a great deal of colour'd glass in the windows.'

Another commentator wrote of the entrance to the churchyard: 'The gateway of Coad is in composition most superb and elegant, the ornaments uncommonly rich, and the whole not at all in accord with the other parts of the building.' It had been made in London, shipped by boat to Ynys Cyngar, and by dint of two determined men (Captain Phillips and John Williams) with a very practical turn of mind, carried to Tremadog and erected before the church, with no damage to its plaster decoration.

Whereas the design of the church was a facsimile of past church design, the design of the chapel, on the other side of the road, and first in view for the visitor, was a tribute to the future. It was perhaps the archetype of hundreds of Nonconformist chapels which were later built through the nineteenth century, with pillars and pediment. Madocks had gone back to his design books and, again with a liking for the Florentine, decided on a symmetrical classical design. The pulpit would be the centre-point, set in the far wall, opposite the big circular window atop the entrance. On its façade, four columns supported the pediment, the two centre ones, each side of the front door, standing free, their rounded shape beautifully plastered.

Robert Pritchard, their best carpenter, was put in charge of building Peniel's roof. He and his team of craftsmen chose the best oak, properly weathered, giving it oil and varnish, fitting it in the space above the congregation as a crown is placed on the head of a monarch.

Chapter 14

Having dealt with the spiritual — the plans for the two places of religion well in hand — Madocks turned to the practical. He wanted more than design in Tan-yr-Allt, he wanted utility. He had heard of a new design for a lavatory but he had never seen one, not even in London. He would have a water closet — a W.C. He knew the man for the job.

"Richard," he said, as four locals stepped aside for him as he approached the smithy, "I want your mind on this application I have for you in Tanny," he announced.

Richard raised his head, puzzled. He had never heard the word 'application' used in this way.

"I want the new way with lavatories. I have heard that they have them in Bath. I want a water closet. We have the old scullery which we can pull down and replace, as you will. We shall need a good supply of water. It washes all away. Not as present when we have to carry it away. Please come up and we shall discuss it. Tomorrow, perhaps?"

Richard took it as a summons and at nine o'clock the following morning he was to be seen striding up the lane towards Tan-yr-Allt. He knew that 'water closet' meant a lavatory in its own room where a water supply sweeps away the droppings. He was thinking about gravity and the cleaning power of descending water. How can we store the sewage? he asked himself. It will have to be in some sort of removable underground container. There would be the corrosive effect; the container would need to be made of a special alloy. It can't be iron; it would rust and rot.

"Somewhere where we can have a drop of water. We need pressure," he said to Madocks as they both stood outside near the slate rock edging the drive. Both men were in some ways of the same cast of mind. They were thinking of the future. Where there was a problem, it could be solved.

"From above," said Richard, as both men looked above the slate into the wood.

At the time, the reservoir receiving water from Llyn Cwm Bach was being finished, to supply water to the mill and factory that were being built between Tan-yr-Allt and the market square.

"Pipe it down from the reservoir," said Richard, with calm confidence. "Bring it down to here," he said pointing upwards, "then we can either build a water closet against that side of the drive, or bring the supply over the drive in a pipe or trough and create the water closet indoors."

Madocks did not want his favoured visitors — house-guests — greeted by a lavatory as they approached the house so they agreed on an in-house WC with water supplied via an overhead pipe. "The pipe will multiply the pressure of water and give us a better cleaning effect," said Madocks.

"There will be plenty of that. The water is coming down some hundred feet," replied Richard.

"It will have to be high," said Madocks. "High enough so that carriages can pass underneath, taking guests to my front door." As always, Madocks had an eye for the social and the effects of first impressions.

"We shall need a soak-away," said Richard. "I'll make a metal container of bronze alloy. On one side there will be a grill for the water to flow out. We'll carry it away in a pipe, down this way." He pointed in a line down the side of the house, "and let it soak away down the bank. The container will be set into the ground next to the house wall. It will have an iron cover. The bronze box will have two turn-up round handles on hinges. To remove it to empty the contents you turn up the handles, insert a shaft through them and carry it away, dumping away from the house. It's a good source of manure, so the garden is the best place."

This was an excellent idea, thought Madocks. He had been worried about smells inside the house. This solution put the material outside.

"And what about the WC?" said Madocks.

"Yes, I have been thinking," said Richard, "simple, really. It all depends on gravity and friction." He had already visualised the design of the overhead water container. "It needs a way of filling the container and not letting the water overflow. It needs a pressure-valve. You have a chain which you pull. That releases the valve. The water rushes downwards and washes-out the bowl, taking the material to this outside box. In the overhead container, there's a float on a stem. The float rises and falls with the water level. As fresh water re-fills the container, the float rises and the cut-off valve works at the end of the stem. Gravity, flotation and friction."

"Excellent," said Madocks. "Draw up a simple plan, specify materials, and a cost schedule. Give it to John Williams. He may decide to put one of his contractors in charge, someone with an eye for water and plumbing. Anyhow, he will make sure the right piping is bought and the rest of the materials. You will direct every stage of the work. Make sure you cost your time and materials properly."

"Agreed," said Richard who already had the whole plan in his mind. They shook hands.

He walked back down the drive and as he entered his smithy he was already looking around for material suitable for the manufacture of the 'foul' container box. The rest of the construction of the new water closet was just manufacture and fitting. Ingenuity came naturally to him.

Chapter 15

The 'hard' side of the town was represented by the two buildings built on land adjacent to the bottom of the drive to Tan-yr-Allt: they were the mill and the Manufactory. They would provide for local employment. Madocks had often written in detail to John Williams about both, their function, design and so on and was much concerned that the Manufactory should have enough power from falling water to drive the carding machines: woollen cloth here made by machinery would be a profitable product.

All this engagement with the business of manufacture had so filled John's mind and energies that in 1808, when Madocks was in 'the borough' as he now was pleased to call it, it was a relief to hear of plans for 'theatre.' He had been influenced by his Wynnstay experience. He said that his two brothers John and Joseph were experienced in theatre and they were looking forward to visiting Tanny (as he called Tan-yr-Allt) and acting in R. B. Sheridan's play *The Rivals.*

Painted panels had come by boat and been stored in a farmhouse outbuilding which had been cleared of straw and the door supplied with a new lock. William had written that he was very concerned about rats: they could eat into the panels and ruin the backdrop of the play. He urged the acquisition of plenty of rat-catching cats; he did not want the rodents anywhere near Tanny, as their smell could come to the sensitive noses of his guests.

The Town Hall was being prepared for the event. There were to be three plays: *The Rivals; Sylvester Daggerwood* and *The Prize.* In the first, John Madocks was to play Fag and Joseph Madocks Sir Anthony Absolute. In the second, William Alexander Madocks played Fustian and in the third all three Madocks brothers appeared. So it was a family occasion and much credit was to be had by them if the occasion proved a success.

The auditorium was to be in the ground-floor room, the arches covered on the inside with heavy cloth. A stage was built behind the adjacent house. Comfortable seats were secured, invitations sent out to families of the district. Madocks made sure that those enthusiasts for theatre came to his house for rehearsals, including Mr & Mrs Massey of Llandecwyn Hall.

The evening came and fortunately it was free of rain and wind; it was a warm August night. There was much bustle in the Market Square with horses and carriages pulling-up, their occupants dismounting. The actors went in to the inn to change into their costume. The audience was greeted by the opened curtain of a doorway by a tall man in a blue coat, a friend of Madocks'. He made great play with his hat doffing, smiled broadly and pretended to know everyone. Another young man took people to their seats. Standing on the steps, waiting to be greeted by the doorman, was John Williams. He had a new coat for the occasion and his white neckerchief was well ironed.

He took his seat. Next to him there was an empty seat. The audience, mostly married couples, were busily chatting away and were in much anticipation of the play, a new venture for their new borough The proscenium arch could have been better, thought John, but it had been manufactured and painted in some haste; its paint was barely dry.

Out of the corner of his eye he saw a young lady. She wore a pale dress in light cream. Around her neck and across her shoulders was a pale blue silky fabric. She was of medium height. She moved sideways along the row, approaching the empty seat next to him. As she made to sit down, her dress made a faint sighing sound.

"Ma'm," he said as he half raised himself from his seat, bowing his head.

"Sir," she replied, with a formal nod.

William Madocks came to the front of the stage and made a short speech. He thanked everyone for coming, hoped they would enjoy the three plays and said that it was all to the credit of their new town, and he hoped it was the first of many. There was much applause, the lady next to him raising her hands unexpectedly high.

It soon became evident to John that she had some connection with the actors. She applauded, responded to and laughed at two of the characters above the others. According to the printed programme, Mrs W. Massey played Lydia Languish and Miss Massey played Julia.

William Madocks acted in the two later plays, where the dialogue was not so sparkling and the plot less sophisticated. However, he entertained the audience with his presence (by this time his waistline had expanded) and his firm control of diction.

"Excellent," said John to Madocks as they gathered in the inn afterwards for drinks, "enjoyed it very much. And so did the audience. Very fine occasion. A tribute to our new town."

"It went well. A few glitches here and there. The set wobbled a bit. But all in all I'd say, a successful start," replied Madocks, looking around the room and seeing three people approaching, "and here come my friends, the Masseys," he said expansively.

"Meet my agent and very good friend, John Williams," said Madocks.

"Very pleased to meet you," said John as they shook hands. Yes, two daughters, he thought. One with a sparkle, one without. The former was Anne.

"You are the young man I have been hearing so much about," she said, moving closer and looking him full in the face.

"Well, I did not think our activities penetrated to the lands beyond the Dwyryd," he said with a smile, proving his good command of English.

"Very much so," she replied. "I have heard so much about you. How you plan to create a great centre here for transport and shipping. How you have built one embankment and plan to build another. How you and Mr Madocks have planned this new town and now a good part of it is built. What remarkable men! What a wonderful scheme!" She was gushing but not silly. She seemed genuinely impressed and enthusiastic.

"You must come and call on us," said Mrs Massey. "Come over for lunch on Sunday."

Madocks looked a little surprised yet pleased that his man had come on so well; that his presence was so good; that he was regarded as an acquaintance of the Masseys, one they would find interesting.

And so it came that the following Sunday John Williams, son of an illiterate farmer from Anglesey, found himself trotting his black gelding through the gateway and along the shingle drive of Llandecwyn Hall. He was greeted with more than politeness. The Masseys knew that some special quality was in this young man. And that they would have no objection to his marrying their youngest daughter Anne, even though he was not of their class. They were sensible enough to know that sometimes quality did not respect class boundaries.

Anne was delightful. She had the kind of beauty that he appreciated and a personality that encouraged exchange and involvement. As a young man from the wilds of Anglesey, he had to create his own style and work at ways of being and saying which were acceptable to a literate family. He had learned quickly, mostly from books.

"There is something very balanced about you. Something settled. I think we shall get on," were her positive words after a week or so of meetings. He was welcome in their house. Anne and he had sat on their drawing-room sofa and were treated as part of the family, which pleased him greatly. One evening he stayed there overnight, after the weather turned for the worst, and in the morning he was delighted to have Anne join him at breakfast, served by a maid who was courteous but not flattering.

Events moved quickly although they did not seem rushed. They seemed to have an inevitability about them, over the months.

One evening, John decided to do the traditional thing. He entered the library, where Colonel Massey was sitting at his desk. Richard moved forwards, raising his hand. Mr Massey shook it warmly.

"I have come to ask for your permission to have the hand of Anne in marriage," he announced with no trace of hesitation.

James looked up, smiling broadly.

"Very good of you," he said, "of course, you have my permission. Let's have a drink."

Two ports were poured on the silver salver and as they raised their glasses, James said, "You both seem happy. I think you are very suited."

This generous remark over-ruled any difference in class. James knew that character was more important than social narrative and that some people learned much quicker, and learned better, than others.

"It will be at the old church of Ynys Cynhaearn, yes?" He was allowing for John's local connections. "I like it there. It has such atmosphere," said James.

The church turned out to be ideal. Because of the first embankment now constraining the sea, access to the church was open at all times, not just, as before, at mid and low tide. The Masseys, parents, uncles, cousins, all squeezed in to the church, and from Anglesey the Williams clan had come in force. On one side of the church, the tailoring was of London. On the other side, the tailoring was of Anglesey. His father was in his new grey suit. His two brothers and sister were there with their chins held high. A bunch of relatives were there, all Welsh-speaking and knowing very little English. The vicar knew some Welsh so he did his best to speak to the Williamses in their language.

Back at Llandecwyn Hall, the bonhomie continued, the two families mixing, smiling as they sat down to dinner, the Williamses and the Masseys side-by-side.

After their wedding the new couple settled in the cottage which John had newly built. It was located just out of Tremadog, on the London Road. It was small but pretty. Its upper windows had irregular panes, its roof had the Madocks shallow angle and outside was a low wall with iron railings. As they lay in bed, their feet pointed to where the first embankment attached itself to Moel-y-Gest.

"Half our work is nearly done but the other half is not done," said John with a worried look. "We did the first embankment. We did the town: nearly finished. Now we do the big task. But I don't know if we'll ever finish this one," he said to Anne as they lay there. He now had someone he could open his heart to.

She turned her head. "It is a great task. But I know these people. They will work for you. They want a Welshman to lead them. I think you will succeed." At that remark, they both slept.

Chapter 16

William Madocks and John Williams stood side-by-side on 'The Green' as William called it, which was the low-lying area between the eight hundred feet tall Moel-y-Gest and Ynys y Towyn. *Ynys* meant island: it was a rocky landform that rose out of the water at the edge of the estuary. Just next to it, the men were working, beginning the groundwork for the embankment.

"A great task," said William.

"Indeed," replied John.

They were both thoughtful, taciturn. They both thought a great deal but they said very little.

William placed his arm across John's shoulders. They could have been brothers. William was taller, more suave. They both had thick-set bodies, dark hair, open faces. John had a sparkle around the eyes. As William looked across the estuary, it was clear that the enormity of their task was on his mind.

"A task of great importance. It will change the area. It is for the good of the people. They will come in and work at it. And I depend on you to make it happen."

They both looked across the estuary towards Penrhyn Isa. It was about a mile away. Building had started on workshops and a tramline led from the shore to the tall rocks.

"Both ends at once is best," said William.

"Yes," replied John, "I know the people at this end but over there, I don't know much about. I had better travel the farms and see if I can raise the labour."

As he spoke, a wagon went past on rails. It contained granite. A tramway had been laid all the way across the Green, curved in the Tremadog direction, ending in the

Llidiart Yspytty quarry, which was part of the estate which Madocks had bought. These wagons were not moving evenly and quickly because the wooden rails on which they travelled were not strong and secure.

"We need iron rails," said Madocks. "I have an idea. We could get them from Thomas Jones of Bersham. I have a share in that works. What would they be like? How do we get them here? Richard Williams, he's the man, I shall ask him."

The two men separated. John made towards a group of men who were trying to re-erect a wagon which had spilled its load. William heard their Welsh-language exchanges.

Richard had not previously been an expert on rails but he quickly warmed to the idea.

"Say they are made of pig-iron, brittle but cheap. And if laid properly, they'll last for ever. Say in lengths not too long; that way, they won't crack. I'll have to see about the dimensions; we'll have to be careful about the cross-section in order to minimise friction when rolling. And how do we get them from Wrexham to here? There's also the question of the gauge."

It was arranged that Richard would go over to Wrexham to explore the idea.

He left his smithy in the capable hands of his assistant Caradog ('C'radog'). Caradog had been getting on well with his boy William who was a sturdy young fellow, whose grey cap and brown britches were seen everywhere in the workshop: the lad had a good sense of self-protection and no fear of fire.

Richard made his way to Rhosllanerchrugog, a mining village a few miles from Wrexham. It was here that Thomas Jones had set his ironworks. The Wilkinson brothers had moved on in Bersham and Brymbo to create more sophisticated manufacturing units, using alloys, making precision tubes, barrels for guns and suchlike. But there was plenty of demand for pig-iron; it was used in the new factories, for trenches in the new canals, as material for girders and side panels for bridges and so on.

As he trotted through Coppi, making for Llwyn Einion, where he had been told the works was, he reflected how industry in places like this, depended on raw materials dug out of the ground. Everywhere around here coal was mined.

As he approached the drive to Thomas Jones' house, he noticed, to his right, a building in local sandstone, its gable end facing the road. High up on the wall was a design picked out in vivid colours. It was in the shape of a sun, circular, with pointed beams coming away from its edge. As he fastened his horse and knocked at the front door of the tall, symmetrical brick house, he noticed the same design etched into the glass in the centre panel, with a Welsh dragon design on another panel.

His discussions with Thomas Jones went well. Jones had heard of Madocks' plans and was keen to participate. He was a no-nonsense sort of a man, gruff, direct and touchy. 'Not good to cross this man,' thought Richard. 'Best to keep things simple and plain and not to get too demanding.' Thomas agreed on the specifications. The lengths of rail were to be four and a half feet long. They had to be fairly short in order to manage the many curves in the line. The rail was to be one and a half inches across. "However," and at this point Richard drew a paper and pencil from his pocket, "I want the top like this." He drew a half circle and about one-third down from top he drew a horizontal line. "This is to secure smooth running," he said, "the roundness will take the wagon easier around curves and the top flat surface will keep the wagon horizontal and form a surface that won't break into the metal of the wheels."

"How many?" Thomas Jones leaned forward. This is where his profit was.

"Two hundred to start with," replied Richard confidently. He knew that he had Madocks' backing to place a secure order.

They agreed a price and in the discussion Jones said he'd place his own wagons and horses at Richard's disposal for the price of one guinea per wagon per day. It was a generous offer from a man who knew that negotiations ending in generosity are more likely to succeed in the long run.

"And will there be more orders?" asked Jones pleasantly.

"Almost certainly," replied Richard, knowing that the embankment itself was about a mile long and the plan was to lay down two lines across it. And in addition, there were the lines to the quarries at each end.

Richard had already decided that the best way of getting heavy loads from Rhos, Wrexham to Porthmadog was by sea. Jones told him that the nearest shipping point was Chester.

"I will send you a message when the pieces are ready," he said.

Richard rode down the drive from Thomas Jones' home. To his left, beyond the field, were two iron smelting works. He could smell the coke burning. As he passed the building which he now realised was the works office, he saw the sun image again, Thomas Jones' emblem. He hoped things would proceed reliably and warmly, as the sun rises and shines.

Chapter 17

A message came to say that the iron rails were ready. Richard had anticipated design and manufacturing problems by carving out, on a piece of wood, a shape which matched the profile of each side of the iron rail. Any deviation from this shape could be disastrous for the smooth running of wheels on the rails. He had iron wheels in mind as well but he had not mentioned their manufacture to Jones in case the casting of the rails was so bad, the business with Jones had to be dropped.

After pleasantries and a glass of port, they walked down to the works, Richard noting that for such a fleshy man, Tom Jones moved with surprising alacrity. He strode past his men with a grunting greeting, the crimson oven in the far corner casting a glow over the brown building.

"There," he said, pointing to a pile of iron rails, "that's them. made last week."

His foreman approached, standing with his hands on his hips.

Richard drew his wooden piece from the deep pocket inside his coat. Tom and his foreman stood up in some surprise. Richard placed it against the side of the rail.

"Good," he said, to the relief of the two concerned observers. And he did it again, this time in a different position.

"Good," again. He did this a dozen times. He tapped the top of one rail. "That one," he said, "not quite right."

"Yes, I'll take that one out," said Jones, summoning two workmen and indicating that rail's removal.

"Generally, pretty good," said Richard. He had tested all the rails and removed seven. "And now we have to work out how to get them moved. We'll take them on your wagons to Chester, and then by sea around to Ynys Towyn. I need a boat."

Tom was in no position to advise on the matter of boats. He was a manufacturer of iron and a very different sort of man to those Cardigan Bay men who had the sea in their blood.

Chapter 18

"Why should we pay to charter a boat when there are men here who can make one?" asked John Williams in his typical we-can-do-it style.

"I can ask Oswald Griffiths," said Richard.

Oswald Griffiths was a boat-builder par excellence. His father was a Barmouth man who had built boats on Barmouth's gently-sloping sands which had stood the test of time and high seas. 'Ozzi' was frequently in Aberdyfi, seeing to passage of people and goods, from the deep-water quay there. Timber was brought in from Germany and Denmark in tall sailing ships.

A message was sent and three days later Ozzi and John Williams were in conversation.

"What do you think, Ozzi. Can we build boats here?" asked John.

"Of course," replied Ozzi, with the optimism born of experience and skill. "Give me half-a-dozen of your neighbourhood carpenters, clear a space; we'll build here just off the beach and finally we'll slide her down."

So the tradition of building sailing-boats for cargo in Porthmadog started in earnest. And not small, half-hearted, boats. These were to be stout, capable and beautiful. They would sail the wind with pride. This corner of Eifionnydd was not for the faint-hearted. Here were big projects calling for big hearts.

"We'll build a ketch," he said proudly. A ketch was simpler and could be built quickly.

"And we shall call her the *Anne*," replied John Williams who had the image of his wife in his mind.

He announced the news to his wife that evening.

"A boat named after me, how wonderful," said Anne Clara. "I am very proud. Can we make the first voyage in it together and sleep in it?"

"The first decent sailing-boat ever to be built here, by hand. We are going to make her a very fine vessel," replied John. "Sails of the best cloth, masts of teak. Brass fittings. We shall sail her to Chester and there you will buy a new dress, to celebrate."

Chapter 19

And so it was, just over three months later, that the ketch *Anne* set off in the dusk from the shores of Ynys-y-Towyn and, with a generous five hands on board, made its way westwards along the estuary of the Glaslyn, heading for Tremadoc Bay. Soon the ketch rocked from side-to-side as the waters of the river Dwyryd, coming in from Penrhyndeudraeth, joined the Glaslyn. John and Anne sat on deck, enjoying the view. Three of the sailors started singing an old sea-shanty that began *'Farwel i Ynys Cyngar.'* John and Anne looked to the rocks along the shore, where, set high on the ridge, was the farmhouse of Garreg Wen Fach, which had a lamp lighting one of its windows. They retired to the comfort of their feather mattress in their small but cosy pine-walled cabin.

The following day, she sailed on the high tide through Caernarfon Bay and the Menai Straits. She passed Caernarfon but did not need to pull in. She passed Bangor, the wind in her sails. She sped across the north coast of Wales, her large mainsail straining. She negotiated the mouth of the Dee, sailed in past Flint, and then entered the five-mile canal. Her entry into the Port of Chester was the subject of admiration by those assembled on the quayside. They saw a workmanlike new vessel with an optimistic upwards curve to her stern and prow, her two masts of polished teak gleaming in the sun.

On the Saltney quay, ropes secured her, fore and aft. Her sails were lowered and tied with stout hemp. John Williams and his wife stepped forward and were helped onto the quay.

"Thank you," she said, throwing a charming look, "it has been an enjoyable voyage." The tanned sailors smiled and clapped their hands gently.

"Now for some shopping," she announced.

He paused and took in the surroundings. Sailing boats were tied up along the curving quay. Masts and rigging hung in the air. Two Hereford bulls were trundling towards them, two boys with sticks leading the way. Irish accents mixed with the Cheshire vernacular. Water slapped against wooden planking and the harbour wall.

"Going to Dublin," said Anne. "What a busy place. Trading . . . sailing. Do you think our area will be like this?"

"I expect so," he replied. "Give it some time. And let's get the big embankment built."

"Ride to town?" said a coachman.

"Very well," said John, "and please take us to overnight lodgings."

The coach took them along the edge of the quayside and into Watergate Street. Anne had never been here before and she was entranced by the tall, elegant, wooden buildings with their elaborate carvings. She admired the 'Rows' which were raised pathways along the streets with buildings over them. The Custom House Tavern seemed a very old building. She saw a sign for 'The Dublin Packet' which reminded her of trade with Ireland.

"Where are we going?" she asked of the coachman.

"I'll take you to *The Bear and Billet,*" he replied. "I believe the fare is good and the beds comfortable."

This man seems to know what he is doing, thought Anne. And when she dismounted in Lower Bridge Street, John pressed a coin into his hand.

"Have a good stay in Chester," he said cheerfully, touching his cap, as John picked up his valise and made for the studded door of the establishment.

Beneath their feet, the ancient planks creaked. Nothing in the building seemed straight apart from the row of windows across the front of the first floor. They sat inside one of these as they were served a full meal of soup, beef with parsnips and potatoes and a pudding of sponge and cream. They had red wine in tall glasses. A wooden platter supported half a loaf and a quantity of butter. What the coachmen had said proved correct. This was an establishment of quality and value. A notice on the wall said that the building dated from 1664, and that it was once owned by the Earls of Shrewsbury who had the sergeancy of the nearby Bridge Gate.

"Tomorrow, we'll sail back. And this will be the first of many trips to bring in goods. Richard will be here with his load of rails. They'll have to load them carefully and balance the load otherwise our *Anne* will sail higgledy-piggledy, off-course," he said.

"Higgledy-piggledy, off-course," said Anne, giggling.

Next morning, she toured the shops, entered one, discussed fashion and the nature of fabrics, and emerged with a new dress. A milliner was next, where she bought a hat, but her main concern were her shoes, which, although well-made by a Caernarfon shoesmith, were not the height of fashion. She found a shoe-shop and emerged with a pair in grey fabric with a green fastening strap in the form of a belt with a tiny brass buckle. She was delighted with them, and they were comfortable. As she sat down in the carriage, she raised her feet, admiring her shoes.

As they approached their boat, with the name *Anne* painted in silver on both sides of her prow, John saw that two wagons were drawn up, their horses munching at oats from their nose-bags.

"Richard," he called out. The dark-haired man in shirtsleeves and waistcoat, with a long face and square chin, looked up and smiled.

"Good to see you John," he replied. "We are loading. Putting the rails in four piles on deck so as to keep the boat balanced."

'Higgledy-piggledy, off-course,' Anne said to herself.

'Lovely man, Richard,' she thought to herself, 'always reliable.'

On board, the iron was being wrapped in canvas and tied down.

"How was your journey from Wrexham?" asked John.

"It's more or less a straight flat route," replied Richard, "from Rhos you come down to Wrexham, make for Gresford and then ford the river Alun in Rossett. I spent the night at the Grosvenor Arms in Pulford. Then a straight route towards Chester, turning down towards this quay in Saltney. Best to use this quay rather than the old one in Chester town."

Richard stepped aboard and examined the four piles of iron. He tested the ropes. They were securely tied. He spoke to his wagon-men. They removed the nose-bags and turned the wagons away from the quayside.

"I shall see you back at the Traeth," he announced, turning towards his grey stallion, "Bon voyage."

At that, with John and Anne standing on deck facing the bustle of the quayside, the two wagons led by the grey moved away. The mainsail was hoisted. The *Anne* struggled to catch the slight wind and very gradually pulled away from the quay, starting her voyage from sophisticated Chester back to the rough lands of Caernarfonshire and Merionnydd.

Chapter 20

In March 1807, at two-thirty in the afternoon and after an ample lunch of chicken and potatoes, Mrs Elizábeth Billington (star of Covent Garden and Drury Lane and according to the *Dictionary of National Biography,* 'the greatest singer England has ever known'), adjusted her bonpoint, presented her face to the sun, stood squarely on the lawn before Tan-yr-Allt and, holding her right hand to her navel, uttered a long, piercing, high note, the likes of which had never been heard before in these uncultured acres. Behind her stood Mr Michael Kelly who had once rehearsed under the great Mozart himself for the first performance of *The Marriage of Figaro.*

Behind them was the ample and smiling figure of Mr William Alexander Madocks, owner of these premises and the Tan-yr-Allt estate and prospective owner of virtually all that he could survey. Once the matter of the building of the Great Embankment had been accomplished.

Below his well-cobbled black shoes was Traeth Mawr, stretched out in virginal display, waiting to be conquered.

His Act of Parliament had been successful. He had lined many palms to ensure that it would be. Its passage was swift and clean. It was a double-edged sword. The Traeth Mawr Bill of February 1807 was written in recognition that its sponsor should benefit in so far as the people of the area and the economy in general should benefit. He would invest in the new embankment. He would pour money into the making of the Cob as fast as sixty wagons of granite a day would drop into seawater and never be seen again.

He was to build the Cob at his own expense. And in return, all the reclaimed land was to be his, and his heirs.

The new embankment would enclose 3,042 acres of sand and marshland. One-fifth of the rent from the cultivated marshland was to be his.

Initial plans had indicated that the Cob was to be 1600 yards long. It was a mile-long sea monster. It would be eighteen feet across at its top and twenty-one feet down from its top to sea-level. At sea-level it was ninety feet across. Below sea-level, it was anyone's guess. There was a depth of sand. But how deep was it? Where was solid rock? Who was to know how deep the sand was and where a firm base was to be found? You just had to keep tipping in the stone and hope for the best.

It was like taking two mountains, chopping them up into rock and rubble and tipping them into the sea. Would that still be enough to construct a causeway?

Faced with equal amounts of happiness of success and horror of failure, the prevailing mood in Tan-yr-Allt was one of determined gaiety. Madocks smiled and smiled and was benign to everyone. He was buying new clothes and his cheeks fleshed out. He was anticipating future wealth and prosperity.

His house parties were a great success. Mrs Billington stood for the prevailing mood. She billowed and she sang, loudly, demanding attention. The culture was one of the expectation of beneficence. Drinks flowed in the drawing-room.

Beneath the stars, guests toasted the new Embankment, located on a strip of sea which below them presented itself in a palette of grey-green.

The house had a Housekeeper, but was short of the required staff. Madocks wrote to John Williams a few days before his arrival, 'I forgot to say that it will be absolutely necessary for you to have some more maids . . . I trust Mary has got a good washer woman from Caernarvon. I can not spare Mary for any work but to superintend the House

Keeper's room & Bed Rooms to see all is clean, and nice every day for the Gentlemen. Towels, water, Beds made, etc. This superintendence will not allow her to do much work. Therefore we must have 2 Housemaids, a Dairy Maid and a washerwoman besides a Kitchen Maid to help the Cook, until the middle of September when we shall be a small family again . . . we shall be 10 persons at least besides servants . . . you must have plenty of Beef ready by the 1st. I hope the larder is in good order.' Poor John Williams must have been rushed off his feet, with the services of someone resembling the later Mrs Beeton required but not available.

Chapter 21

The great task of taming the Glaslyn, capping Traeth Mawr and bringing cash into Madocks' pockets started in March 1808.

John Williams had paced the distance needed on the shoreline. He had stood close to the rocky island Ynys y Towyn holding two sharpened metal rods. He thrust one into the ground, turned his back and paced forty steps. That would make about ninety feet. He looked up across the misty estuary. He thought, 'From here we need to drive it straight across to Penrhyn Isa.' In the distance he saw grey streaks where the slate rocks were located, only some thirty feet back from the shore. They were lucky. These rocks were ideal for footings. They would start the blasting and carrying as soon as possible. At this end, the Madocks quarry at Llidiart Yspytty was of granite. The tramway was partly completed and now that they had iron rails, carriage by wagon was much more successful.

On the ninth day of March, twenty-one men lined up. They put their spades in the ground and threw the earth backwards. Another gang, behind them, with wheelbarrows (the same wheelbarrows as those used to construct the first embankment) carried the material to the base of the rocky island, where it was spread out. They left two yards width of earth holding back the water, and when they had dug some twenty feet, stone was called for from the rows of wagons which had been filled in preparation. This trench secure, the two yards of earth was broken into and the sea flowed in against the new stone. Two rows of rails were extended over the newly-laid rock, the wagons rolled along them, and the stone tipped into the sea.

Progress was good. Madocks thought that the whole task could be over in six months. But he was very wrong.

One night, John Williams went cold as he thought of the project. 'Alright close to shore,' he thought, 'but that is where the estuary is shallowest. The tides would have least effect there. But in the centre section, the force of the water against the underwater sand would be much greater and the erosion powerful.' His final, chilling, thought was, '. . . the sand could be fifty feet below the waterline and base rock fifty feet below that. Oh my God.'

Talking to Anne that night, he said, "We are going to have problems. Big ones. Already progress is slower as the water deepens. We'll have to find a way of tipping in more stone. I wonder if Richard has an idea."

Conversations with Richard Williams, blacksmith and inventor, took place the following day. Richard had his eye fixed on the distant Penrhyn rocks.

"They're pretty close to where we start the causeway. And they are tall. I wonder if we can build something using gravity, getting the rock into the sea in a quick way. I'll ride over there and have a good look."

John was cheered by this positive move and when Richard returned the following day, he had a plan.

"We need a moving belt. That will carry the slate down and partly outwards. Then with the help of an engine and a series of cogs, the belt would carry the slate and drop it into the sea. As the stone builds up underwater and comes above the surface, the belting and cogs would be extended and that way a series of heaps would be created. I reckon we could make it. I'll call it *The Penrhyn Machine.*"

Richard was a master of wheels, cogs, belts, chains and canvas and quite soon the contraption was being assembled against the Penrhyn rock and down towards the shore. In practice it was found necessary to apply the Penrhyn Machine twice, side-by-side.

Consequently, the Penrhyn side of the construction made better progress than the Ynys-y-Towyn side, where the source of newly-cut rock was much farther away.

A new source of stone was found. It was at Tuhwnt i'r Bont, at the back of Moel y Gest, just off the Pwllheli road. A rail track was laid and soon two separate rail lines carried stone-filled wagons to the embankment, which was demanding more and more stone tipped into the hungry jaws of the sea. The stone was disappearing at an alarming rate. At the Towyn end, over fifty wagon-loads a day were rolled over from the quarries and tipped into the sea.

The task of creating the Causeway took three years and three months, from March 1808 to June 1811. It was backbreaking, repetitive, onerous. Welshmen and Irishmen worked from seven in the morning until seven at night. Wagons brought rock from the three quarries. It was dumped into the sea and they carried on dumping until the grey peak of the stone started to appear just below the surface water, like the face of some monster born under water and appearing to the world for the first time.

In these thirty-nine months of work, through over a thousand days, we could reckon that some fifty-five thousand wagon-loads of rock were released into the Glaslyn. As the work proceeded, it was as John Williams had predicted, the space under the sea's surface got deeper and deeper. More and more rock was needed to fill the void. Some days, John thought they would never finish it. But, being the man he was, he persisted. Money continued to come from Madocks' diminishing resources. Each day, dozens of men lined up by the door of John's newly-built office close to the rocky island, expecting their wages. They were rewarded by money in their hands but little in the nature of satisfaction, when a whole month would pass and the causeway had proceeded only a few feet.

Sometimes John would stand at the space where the

causeway started, looking at the work, the men in their shirts, braces and tied-up trousers, the sounds of rock falling and the rolling of wagons, and wondered at what made these people the way they were — loyal, determined, fixed in their purpose to finish a job they had started. For many centuries, he knew, their kin had survived in these mountains. They had lived hand-to-mouth and whatever success came their way, it was because they had a purpose, worked supremely hard and when the job was done they had the quiet satisfaction that they had survived and succeeded, despite deprivation, condescension, disparagement and obscurity.

From them, in the evening as dusk was settling, and as they wearily walked back with their spades, there came a light mist into the air from their bodies, a rising veil of masculinity, commitment and morality.

Chapter 22

Yet — as God is the Great Equaliser — an extraordinary thing happened. As the cap on the Glaslyn grew from both sides of the estuary, the pressure on the river altered and intensified. It started to respond, as a snake responds when it searches for a way through a thicket. It started to turn sideways: it swung to the right, towards Ynys-y-Towyn.

In six months after the start of building, the rocky island was feeling a new neighbour. Fresh water was newly flowing across its shanks. After another year, the newly energised Glaslyn had scooped away a substantial amount of soil, rock and sand.

After two years, a ten feet deep hole had been created and after three years the hole was large enough to create a pool large enough to accommodate ships. Thus Porthmadog harbour was born, location for the export of slate and home of dozens of magnificent schooners.

In the summer of 1810, Madocks addressed John Williams, "I cannot allow the chapel to be delayed. I know we need more and more men to finish the embankment. But it would be a shame on me if I allowed it to come before the chapel. Peniel has to proceed. See to it."

John Williams was surprised at the abruptness of the instruction. But sometimes Madocks could be like that. Most of the time he was charming and accommodating, but at some times he was sharp and to-the-point.

John returned to the embankment. He saw four men sitting on a stone. Three were eating their bread and cheese but the fourth was writing. He had a sheaf of paper in his left hand; paper rose out of the left pocket of his large coat. On his head he had a large sack-coloured hat which covered a woollen head-cover. His head was bent down and his writing moved quickly.

"Twm," said John, addressing the stooping figure, "would you like to go to Peniel to help out for a couple of weeks? The walls need finishing and the pediment is only half done."

"Of course. It is my pleasure. An act of God, for God," replied Twm, smiling. He spoke good English. "For you, John, I'll build a new town. Much better than this dragging and dumping of stone. It goes on and on. But I'll need to get back to see to the laying of dressed stone along the side, and the grouting. We need to do a proper job."

"Take somebody with you," said John, acknowledging Twm's superior status among the labourers and masons.

Twm rose to his feet, his long coat rippling in the wind. "This young man," he said, putting his hand on the shoulder of a tall, thin, twenty-year-old from Garn, "he can reach much further than I can."

They departed in the direction of the new town, chatting in Welsh about chapels and plastering. The presence of good quality concrete was of some concern; it was necessary for smooth, waterproof rendering.

In Peniel, the external finish was of the best quality.

When the day came to open the chapel, Madocks and a number of relatives sat in the front pews. John Williams and Anne sat by them. Close to Madocks was the prominent hunched figure of Twm o'r Nant, complete with eccentric headgear and the same long coat he wore for work. Thomas Charles from Bala, the famous evangelist, took the sermon: he spoke of building and achievement and God's work on earth. When Twm went forward to present his reading, it was full of wit, dialogue and humour. This was his usual style. His 'interludes' were known all over Wales. He was not one of those elite literati who prided themselves on the excellence of their *cynghanedd.* He wrote for the entertainment of the ordinary people. He was an early Charles Dickens. His plays and recitations poked fun at everybody, celebrated current events, including enough drama to draw the audience in.

Twm and Madocks got on well. A portrait of Twm, which had been exhibited at the Royal Academy in 1799, hung in Tan-yr-Allt. It was by the Ruthin artist Edward Pugh. Madocks bought it, feeling that he and Twm had something in common. He was a writer for the people and Madocks was a planner for the people. Both had contributed to the making of Peniel.

Chapter 23

The monster was finished in the third week of July, 1811. It had emerged from the sea in instalments and as the final two end-faces were linked together by a final crashing of dropping stone, the water on each side lapped and twisted as if not accustomed to this blocking of the usual flow. Shouts of *"Dyma ni,"* *"Da iawn,"* and *"Wedi gorffen"* came from the lips of men who had hammered away at the task over the last three years, heaving and pushing, lifting, throwing, setting stone, grouting, all in the face of a disturbed and sometimes very angry sea.

Hats were thrown in the air. For once, it was a fine day. Hammers were knocked on wheelbarrows. There was much handshaking. Three men stood on the fresh stone. They leaped forward in unison, landing on the Penrhyn side. One shouted, *"Mae hi wedi gorffen."* And another said, rather more profanely, *"Mae'r diawl i lawr."* ('The devil is down.')

A large lady wearing a yellow bonnet was seen negotiating the embankment, carefully placing her feet between the jutting rocks. Beside her were her two children, boy and girl.

John Williams, who had been standing there in a state of quiet satisfaction and some relief, greeted her with enthusiasm.

"All the way across. Mrs Maggie Jones, you are the first ordinary person to cross the Cob, from Penrhyn to Ynys-y-Towyn. Congratulations. You are invited to our celebration party."

"My brother Gareth lives over there," she said, pointing to a cottage. "Now I can see him every week. We shall go to Peniel together on Sunday. This is a great thing you have done, John. It will bring us all together. And Gareth shall have more neighbours, for even now new houses are going up. Soon we shall have a town. And we shall call it *Williamstown.*"

Her urging was a flattery to John Williams, who smiled in appreciation. He would not know it now, but a name was soon to be attached to the area where the houses were now being built; not his name, but that of his boss.

And he was in deep financial trouble.

In February he had been cheerful. He wrote from Boston saying he would be down the following week with '. . . money to buy all the Boats you can engage.' But his creditors were circling: 'It is not impossible that John Ellis may plague you for a day or two in the beginning of next week. But do not let that, or any thing dishearten you: on my return to London I shall settle it . . . then off to Wales to put all into Action . . . never mind these Fellows. We shall conquer them."

When Madocks appeared at the Traeth in April, he was very lame. His gout was worsening. A month later he wrote: 'My whole soul is now entirely bent on closing the Bank. Great works are achieved by Conductors being alive while others are asleep. Every Evening and night should be employed in preparing to go to work next day. The precious hours in the morning should be made the most of by the workmen . . . Make a bargain with yourself not to think of anything till the Bank is done."

More money was available, but it was not to go to the creditors. Madocks wrote, 'Be sure you do not apply one shilling of Mr Oakden's £500 to John Ellis or John Evans his solicitor but pay up the Men with it. Devote it to the Men."

After completion, the North Wales Gazette ran the headline COMPLETION OF THE EMBANKMENT AT TRE-MADOC, writing, 'To attempt to enter into the merits of the individual gentleman (W. A. Madocks Esq.) who has finished the great work, amidst difficulties incalculable to the

common mind, we feel ourselves inadequate to the task . . .'
In the account, Madocks was compared with 'New River
MYDDELTON.'

The paper's account continued, ' . . . the lower orders
immediately with the native ardour of their ancestors, on Mr
Madocks' approach, took his horses from his carriage and
triumphantly drew him over the embankment, which was,
comparatively speaking, the work of his own hands.'

At the end of July, as he was supervising the flattening of
the top of the embankment John stood and looked across the
Traeth. He spoke to a workman standing next to him, "Where
is the Glaslyn going? You see," he said, pointing with his
finger, "it is lingering over there. If it does not entirely move
that way (he pointed to Ynys-y-Towyn), we will not be able to
turn the Traeth into pasture. And (he said quietly to himself)
Madocks will not get his money."

His companion said, "We have done the work. Let's hope
the river obeys."

John Williams wrote to Madocks a week later that the
sluice next to Ynys-y-Towyn was working and that the Traeth
over its main part was drying. He did not mention that the
Glaslyn was still flowing on its original route and was a
severe impediment to the reclamation of the estuary.

Chapter 24

The coachman handed John Williams a canvas bag tied with string. He sat down at his desk and being an economical man, rather than cutting the string with a scissors he untied it with his fingers. He wrapped the string into a ball and dropped it in one of the boxes he kept for odds-and-ends. Inside was a bundle of advertising leaflets, printed in Lincoln's-in-the-Field, London. 'Another one of my master's schemes,' thought John as he glanced through the text. 'Jubilee' was a grand word. He reached for his dictionary, which told him that its origins was at the time of the early Jews, who every fifty years had a celebration to mark their deliverance from Egyptian slavery. English monarchs had such a commemoration on the fiftieth year of their reign. Not much of this in Meirionnydd, in this sparse place with little history, he thought, but perhaps slavery — slavery through poverty. But we must pick up, he thought. We must make a new future for ourselves. He looked out of the window. The sky was blue; the seagulls were in good voice. The finishing touches were being applied to the Embankment. A man walked across his window carrying on his shoulder a length of iron rail.

1811 had so far been a good year. The embankment had been finished, although it had taken a very long time. Toil and trouble had ended and each day proud walkers were to be seen traversing it.

He read the flyer again. 'An OX will be roasted upon the Middle of the Embankment.' Fine, thought John, but what do we do if it's raining? Well, we'll roast it in Tremadog square, he thought, under an awning. The key week was the third week in September. That was the week of jubilee, now a word for celebrations. There will be an ordinary.

"Jim," he called-out, "what is an 'ordinary'?" His assistant, although a Welshman from Caernarfon, used to work in an inn and knew English ways.

"It's when you lay on a plate of food, the same for everybody, and everybody pays the same price for it, quite cheap."

Fine, thought John, we have the Madoc Arms in Tremadog, managed by the Lewises. We'd better make sure they have enough food and staff.

A letter came from His Master the following day. It was in his usual casual style, in his spidery writing. It said of how he had been up to the Humber and inspected 4000 acres of '. . . particularly well-irrigated land . . . recently reclaimed . . .' He wrote, 'The Improvement of Warping is most astonishing. I shall however reserve full particulars till I see you.' We'll better have a full discussion on this, thought John, for neither he or his trusty Jim had any idea what 'Warping' was. At the back of his mind, John thought of the line of the Glaslyn, which he had kept to himself. He got out of his chair and looked out of the side window, towards Minffordd. The tide was out. The Glaslyn was running down that side. Bad news, thought John. The whole traeth is still very wet, even at low tide. Some magic needs to be done if this three thousand acres is to be turned into pasture, fit for renting. Mr Madocks' pockets are going to suffer, he thought to himself. But Madocks had his dreams and he didn't want to interfere with those.

Madocks' optimism and good nature were in full flow. He wrote, 'I write this principally to Urge you, and to press on you the propriety of having the Addition to the House ready by the 28th of this month and that all workmen must be out and all cleared away behind, and all neat. I am aware that the Bed Room plaister will not be ready for use for some days though we must use every artificial means of drying them by the Races which I have postponed on the second account till the 9th, 10 & 11th September . . . For Goodness Sake, Loose not a moment. The time gets every hour more precious . . . Let us Shew off . . ."

Jim's mare was stamping her feet outside. John turned to Jim, "Go over to Tan-yr-Allt and if Rowlands is not there, have a word with his man. Tell him that Madocks is champing at the bit and wants the house finished in the next fortnight. And he wants it all cleaned out and tidy because his important guests will be there."

The next letter John received signalled that Madocks was thinking about his potential income from lettings and the crucial matter of water flow, "Your letter of the 9th which I have just met with on my return from Boston gives me sincere pleasure. I long to hear though the particulars of the High Tide running through the Sluice . . . I long to be with you for the remainder of the Season. All the world will attend our Jubilee. Stick the Hand Bills all over the County.'

'. . . our Jubilee,' thought John. Marvellous what a simple pronoun suggests and contains.

Two small boys were summoned. They had their caps on and stout boots. John handed the taller of the two a wad of handbills, a pot of paste and a paint-brush. *"Yn bob man,"* he instructed. The boy looked around at the new walls, half-finished road and half-built cottages. *"Bob man,"* he repeated, raising his paint-brush. They had been instructed to place them everywhere and soon the area was peppered with hand-bills.

Races were foreign to John. He had no idea how to make a racecourse. However, a later letter from his Boss clarified things by moving them to the responsibility of someone else, which was very much his style. Humphrey Owen was to 'actually make the course.' He did arrive and was much as expected, all polished leather and brown bowler-hatted. He echoed Madocks' words about Carriages and Gentleman. As he trotted off in the direction of Morfa Bychan, John wished him good luck. But as the area was mostly sand, scrub and thin grass, with thousands of rabbits, John set a team of five men at his disposal, experts in spade-work, and soon a track free of rabbit-holes was created, well-flattened-out.

Looking forward to the week of the Jubilee and not at all daunted by having to set all the practical arrangements, John left his office that evening in a sanguine mood. He mounted his horse and as he was drawing at the reins, he noticed an unusual figure some hundred yards away. He was a small, fat, man in a black coat. He was holding a paper and making marks on it. He was moving along the newly-laid iron rails. John pulled away. It was only later that the significance of what he had seen struck him. A lawyer, a clerk, a debt-collector. He was listing Madocks' assets in preparation for seizure through the courts. He had seen the precursor, the one figure who out-stepped the rest, and the others were soon to follow, as ravens circle a dead lamb. Preparations for the Jubilee had, in John Williams' mind and heart, a certain dread hidden behind them.

Chapter 25

William Thomas, up in Ysgubor Goch, had determined to make a contribution. His pride in being the best farmer in the vicinity brought to his mind the picture of his best young bull, excellent for beef-on-the-bone. Butchered two weeks before the event, its carcase hung in one of his well-aired outhouses. Early on Monday, the sixteenth of September, 1811, Richard came up, pulled a cart next to the door and with another well-muscled man, unhooked the carcase from the beam and laid it sideways in the cart. His journey down through Penmorfa and Tremadog was reminiscent of celebrations after a brutal encounter in Ancient Rome. Youngsters waved and peeked into the cart. Their elders smiled. Richard passed John Williams' house (which they were soon to leave for a grander one) and directed his towing horses on to the new embankment. People lined the route; they were mostly workmen and as he passed they raised their hats and spades in celebration.

A fire had been prepared. An iron spike was pushed through the carcase, a handle in metal attached to one end. The rod rested in greased iron cradles at both ends, held by stout oak crossed timbers. Richard, of course, had knocked-up this contraption in no time, including a suspended metal tray that held the fire, allowing air to get in underneath it. The kindling, sticks and timber were laid and ready. Richard stood back, waiting. Then he saw the black carriage. It trundled over the embankment and stopped, between cheering crowds. Madocks stepped out. He looked particularly handsome and grand, in grey trousers with spats, a silk waistcoat and a frock coat with glossy lapels. Richard had prepared a lighting-stick in the form of a light wooden pole with linen fabric tied to the end. In a bucket he had placed a mixture of tar and petroleum.

He raised the pole. Madocks raised his right hand. They clasped one another's hands. The pole dipped into the bucket. A box of vestas was produced and the flame set to the linen. The flame leaped in the air. Smiling broadly, they held the pole in the air, ready to ignite the wooden fragments below the carcase of the ox.

"We will celebrate the completion of a great enterprise," said William in his grandest style. "We have worked together, Richard and his men, John Williams and his men and all our other fine workers. With their sweat, with their energy and dedication, we have driven back the sea. Let us have a week of celebration."

With that, the flame was applied and the fire quickly took hold. A light wind helped it and soon the ox was dripping fat, which further helped the fire. Two men held the handle and the carcase slowly turned.

John Williams and Anne stood by, looking well pleased, but out of the corner of his eye, John saw that the Glaslyn was still lapping the shore below Minffordd. He also recalled the unusual man counting the metal rails.

As they left the site, the slight wind continued. Men were posted to continue turning the spit, which they did in relays for the remainder of the day and through all of Monday night. The area was impregnated by the smell of roasting ox. It was as an incense which accompanied the events in and around the Tremadog church which started at ten o'clock the following morning.

Pageantry. William Madocks, squire, landowner, benefactor, loved pageantry. He had invited as many grand folk as he could muster and he had their carriages lined up outside the church. The church was full, with dozens outside. They listened intently and sang enthusiastically. Prayers were read by the Revd Martin Sheath of Boston, whose intoning cadences were of a music previously unheard by the Nonconformists who frequented the chapel across the road. A Choral Service was performed under the direction of Dr Pring of Bangor. As the good folk stepped out from the impressive church and made their way towards the gateway, a band broke into music. *Men of Harlech* was a little shaky but nonetheless enjoyable. The carriages were stepped-into, swayed a little and moved, depending on the mood of their horses. Then, to the joy and surprise of all, the new suits stepped forward. These, in grey striped wool, were worn by men moving forward three abreast, forming a line that reached back nearly to the Town Hall. Again, this was due to the munificence of Madocks who had contacted some six tailors across the north-west and had sent each one a length of cloth, the name of the wearer and his essential measurements. Jim had organised this. He knew two tailors in Caernarfon, which was a good start. Some two months earlier, each working man in turn had been required to lay off for half-an-hour, enter the side door of the office and had himself measured by two ladies, who had some giggles when legs had to be measured for new trousers.

Meanwhile in the Sheriff's office in Caernarfon, a number of orders to distrain Madocks' goods had been received and were being acted upon. Men of minor character had been sent to do the auditing, and their reports, on dozens of sheets of foolscap paper, occupied a wooden tray on a counter in a back office.

The celebrations continued. The band puffed, walked and played. Sometimes, as their repertoire was limited to five pieces, they played the same piece over again a number of times. The carriages were parked on the Green, the occupants stepping-down into a terrain none of them had ventured into before. However, the band and the men in suits marched as the smell of ox drew them forward. On the new embankment, tables had been laid-out with plates, cutlery, and an ample supply of foodstuffs in bowls. The ladies of the table, all looking splendid in cream cotton and blue bonnets, served food and wine. The ladies and gentlemen, having successfully walked the rough ground of the embankment, were served first and had chairs to sit on. The butcher, in traditional apron and hat, sliced away at the carcase, trying to allocate the quality of the cut to the social class of the diners. The band earned a rest as they chewed and drank. The grey-suited workmen stood in line to one side, quiet and dignified, as the plainer-looking of the ladies handed out victuals to them, with a chicken leg for each and one slice of beef.

One lady, comfortably seated, raised her hand. "All this for Madock," she said as she gazed over Traeth Mawr in the direction of Snowdon.

"Indeed," replied her companion, "he is going to be a very wealthy man when all this is drained and rented-out. And I believe his name is Madocks."

But of course Madocks in his mind was a very wealthy man already, in anticipation of profits. But the thought and the deed had some space between them; a space of some three thousand acres of dank, undrained, land, much contaminated by salt water.

The diners withdrew, a little louder and less stable due to the effects of food and wine. "To the races," was shouted. "Forward. Fast horses. Racing and betting."

They entered their carriages with alacrity. Their horses moved forward, travelled down High Street and turned up to the left towards Morfa Bychan. Their carriages struggled over the hill. Their occupants saw the long beach in front of them and anticipated fast times. Two bookmakers, one extremely fat and wearing expansive check, saw the oncoming procession and mentally tagged each at twenty pounds, deficit to them, profit to me. They were not far out because by five-thirty, their leather bags were laden with notes and coins.

Four races were run, with some eight horses in each. The nobility of the north-west had come forward with their best bloodstock, with Lord Penrhyn having the most winners. The Wynnstay stables were well represented, much to Madocks' pleasure.

The Ordinary followed, at the Madoc Arms. It was crowded. William Madocks stood at the door, ushered his people in and saw them comfortably seated. The ox by this time had given up its best slices but some fatty bits remained. They were delivered to the diners with announcements that the ox had been bred in the best acres of William Thomas, farmer of Ysgubor Goch. There was much appreciation.

The Town Hall, next door to the Madoc Arms, began to change its façade as the outside light faded and a warm glow issued from the building. In the upstairs dancing room, the five-piece orchestra, squeezed into a tiny balcony high up on the inside wall, broke into vigorous tune with many waltzes. The ladies with their long dresses (changed into at the Arms) swerved and progressed as elegantly as they could and their companions, rounded men of proportion, who had lost money at the races, tried their hardest to be fine and dandy.

Below, on the slate floor of the Town Hall, open to the elements but for the pillars between the open archways, the locals, workmen and friends danced somewhat less elegantly to the sound of a local fiddler, harpist and an aged accordion player, who suddenly fell asleep between chords, head down in his wooden armchair.

Wednesday was Eisteddfod day. There was a great deal of talk and self-importance. There were Bards — a special species. W. A. Madocks, Esq; presented a valuable cup to Mr David Own of Llanystymdwy for the best Welsh poem on Agriculture. There were five other poems recited, all of which had merit. A harper called Hercules won a silver cup, beating his four rivals who were, through the enthusiasm of the audience, awarded a share of a collected £10.

Over in Morfa Bychan, after the horses were fed, watered and rested, the races continued. More money was lost and more bookies went home happy.

The *North Wales Gazette* had a field day. Their adjectives flew and their rhetoric expanded close to bursting: 'We congratulate the public at large on the completion of a work which stands unrivalled in the history of the world. That a single individual should attempt, persevere in, and at last (after four years exertion) accomplish so stupendous an undertaking appears truly astonishing! And it only requires ocular demonstration to convince the incredulous of its superiority over every other work of the kind now extant. We felt particularly happy in witnessing so full an attendance of our Cambrian Nobility, Clergy and Gentry; and we do not hesitate to predict that future ages will hail the day that gave birth to the enterprising W. A. Madocks Esq. whose family motto has, by undaunted exertions, been so amply verified: NON MIHI SOLUM."

During the week of the Tremadoc Jubilee, a comet was seen on successive nights, tearing through the sky, just before midnight. Those of a Shakespearean cast of mind will see this as symbolic. Brightness, celebratory, repeated. And perhaps as a portent, that the future might hold something different from the confidence and security enjoyed during the Jubilee week.

Chapter 26

1812.

John Williams and Anne had moved into Tan-yr-Allt. The house now had a staff of only four because in the absence of Madocks, house-parties and celebrities, it had no need of show and extravagance. John felt no embarrassment in moving into his master's space, for his position in society had so risen in the last three years that he was considered equivalent of a Squire. And Madocks was so embroiled in the affairs of Westminster and that of the new town of Boston that he was away from Tremadog for months at a time.

The house had an extensive view over Traeth Mawr. Hardly had the Williamses finished unpacking their goods and establishing a daily routine than Anne noticed a change in the weather. Over the sea and behind Moel-y-Gest there was usually a patch of silver and blue towards the end of the day, before dusk. This was accompanied by a light westerly wind. The curtains against the windows caught this light and they swayed a little as the wind caught them. Then on February the thirteenth, the silver light vanished, the wind rose and the windows had to be kept firmly shut as it increased. A strange and unusual colour appeared in the sky through the day, a dark pinky-brown, the colour of wet sand. Anne and John stood inside the french window under the veranda. The trellis-work, although fastened together by the strong stems of climbing roses, was moving vigorously.

"I think there is a heavy storm at sea," said John, "the westerlies are rising in the equinox period. This is just the start of it. If it's really bad it could last many days." As he spoke, the taller trees growing in the sloped bank below the house moved before the wind, left to right, left to right.

Later in the day, the wind increased and every now-and-then there was an unusual short scream, a sound similar to that of air being forced through a narrow tube. Two days passed and the weather worsened. Freezing cold set in and the landscape hardened with frost. Rain and snow fell and when the rains fell in torrents, Traeth Mawr filled with rainwater which failed to soak into the hard ground. Storms gathered, bringing in a swollen sea, battering the new embankment.

John and Anne occupied a bedroom at the rear of the house, facing the hill. The two best bedrooms at the front were empty. Ice gathered inside their bedroom window. John had asked the housekeeper to light a fire each day to warm the room. As they lay in bed, preparing for sleep, the roar of the wind increased. Then there was a loud puff and then the sound of falling glass. John leaped out of bed, entered the best bedroom and saw particles of glass lying across the green chaise longue. The curtains were twisted and partly collapsed. There was a hole in the top half of the casement window.

"The wind has blown through the window," he shouted. "We need some help."

He brought two of the staff in from the adjoining building. They covered the window with planking and canvas, swept-up the glass and re-hung the curtains.

At six in the morning, there was a loud and insistent knocking at the rear door. John threw on his light overcoat and opened the door. The man who stood there, hunched, soaking wet, was David Davies. He knew him well. He lived in one of the new stone houses that bordered the green and the new harbour.

"Sir," he announced, "Sir, it is bad. The embankment has given. The sea is all in. All over Traeth Mawr there is flooding. Serious flooding."

The poor man was short of breath. John took him in,

helped him to remove his outer garments, re-kindled the fire in the kitchen and sat him down before it to warm.

Davies was upset. He had worked at the embankment for the past years and regarded it as practically an extension of his home and family. His eyes had an abandoned look.

"How much has gone?" asked John.

"Hard to say. I couldn't see much. All very wet and windy and spray everywhere. I could see that it was a breach because the water was high up against the quay-wall."

Outside, the gale continued. There was a swishing from the trees above the drive and the back door was thumping in its frame.

"We'll need to get there," said John. "are you well enough to ride?" David Davies had walked all the way to Tan-yr-Allt because he did not own a horse.

"I'll ride," he said.

John went upstairs and told the news to Anne.

"This is bad," he said. "This may be catastrophic."

Anne looked him full in the face, "Go to it. Take care of yourself."

They dressed themselves in deep hats and long overcoats. In the stables, they found the horses alert: they had not liked the night with its howling wind. Saddles and bridles were set and they rode, heads down, against the prevailing wind. The quay was a swirl of spume. The sky was as if filled with angry dragons. Their horses wanted to go no further as they approached the start of the embankment. They tied their horses and walked. Against them the wind was as a strong firm hand, pushing them backwards. They managed some thirty yards along the embankment and then a break in the clouds gave them a picture of how it was. The breach was some forty feet long. On the land side were piles of stones, large and small. They lay against one another in disorder. The top wall was completely gone and the footings had been ripped out below sea-level. On the sea side, a swell was humping itself against the embankment wall as if trying to obliterate it. John thought that the embankment was at risk and they might be swept away with it. Davies and he knew that they could not be heard against the wind's noise. They both turned their backs to the wind, bending. John waved his arm towards Ynys y Towyn, indicating their withdrawal from this scene of destruction.

"Go home," said John as they unfastened the horses, "take the mare with you and see her well protected. I will ride back to Tanny and make preparations. We have big work to do."

Chapter 27

The storm exhausted itself.

The sluice-gate had been well made and carried a huge quantity of water away from the flooded Traeth Mawr, through the new quayside and out to sea. William sat down at a desk in Tan-yr-Allt and penned the following letter:

Tan-yr-Allt
February 26, 1812

Sir,

You have doubtless before now been made acquainted with the dreadful result of the High Tides upon the TRE MADOC EMBANKMENT, which I am sorry to say has placed almost the whole Undertaking in a most perilous situation . . .

Though you are distant from the spot where this catastrophe has taken place and though I am unknown to you, and likewise my Friend and Employer, yet still I have that confidence, that any Friend to the country which has given him birth, will not accuse me in taking this liberty, which I humbly confess, far exceeds the bounds of propriety: My Employer is far from home and was, in course, unprepared to meet this event; and it is totally beyond my power to collect one half of the number of men and teams, that are really necessary to save the Concern, in so short a time as the nature of the accident requires, I have thus taken the liberty of soliciting your aid: the support that can be effectual to us at this moment is comprised in Manual Labour, Horses and Carts.

Should, therefore, this my solicitation have its desired effect, any time in the course of the ensuing week (or even a week following) will not be too late for you to lend us your assistance.

Such of our Friends as may be disposed to aid us, may rely upon their Servants and Horses being properly taken care of, in suitable food and provender, in case they should stay with us more than one day.

I am,

Sir,

Your most obedient humble Servant,

JOHN WILLIAMS

(Agent to Mr. Madocks)

This was a truly fine letter, treading the delicate line between obeisance and pleading. And not over-doing the latter.

It had a remarkable effect.

Firstly, it was copied repeatedly by Charles Pace, the clerk in the embankment office. Pace had been a butler; he had the stooped, faux-courteous, manner of the type. His work at his desk was equally timely and subservient. He liked nothing better than copying documents. His pen flowed and beside him the copies piled up.

Mr Cadwaladr Owen of Garndolbenmaen wrote the following:

Mr J. Williams. Mr Madock Aidg. Tanyralldent. Febry 1812. From Mr Cadr Owen, Dolbenmaen.

Kind Sr

It was to leat lasd nite to send letters but Ive send my son with them be for day lite and before non of them was up: I am very sorry Ive only 2 hors. I hope son in Law can assissd me for one hors — your Berar did not speak with me — wether he has been at Tyddun mawr Dolwgan Rwng y ddwurud & sow forth where is good Teams Ive nomore but wishing you sugsesfull and good faithful Nibaures in the disdress your sincear Humble sarvant and well wisher

CADR OWEN

This remarkable letter, written under much strain and purpose, typified the response from 'Nibaures' — neighbours — who were anxious that the great project should not be lost, for its success was of benefit to everyone. Lord Penrhyn was listed as sending 300 men. A Colonel Peacock from Anglesey sent, '7 Men and 2 Carts and Horses, to remain with you a week . . . I have given Money to my Husbandmen to subsist them: at two shillings a day each, and I allow the same pay, besides, as if they worked for me at Home — I mention this to you to prevent you giving them any money."

The response of men, horses and carts was remarkable. They flooded into Tremadog, where John had posted men on the streets and outside the town to direct the incomers to where they were needed. The iron rails on the causeway had disappeared (presumably to pay creditors) so the task of filling the breach was made much worse by the absence of trolleys on rails to carry the stones to the gap in the causeway which was virtually in its centre. At the end of the day, men from outside the district would report to the office and be directed to their beds for the night. Practically every dwelling had a non-paying lodger and horses and carts were parked in untidy order.

The terrible weather continued through February and March. News came from London that the Thames was frozen over and that a Frost Fair was held on the ice. From the other end of the Kingdom, in Edinburgh a foot of snow fell. On March 18th, Spring Tides were at their worst. The severe cold continued.

Madocks' financial affairs were collapsing by the day. His main creditor, Girdleston, was owed £30,000. On March 24th, he levied £14,500 on the debt. Lawyers, clerks and bailiffs were descending on Tremadog like the black remains of a burning fire carried in the air. Morale was shrinking. A bailiff called Sharpe stuck a paper on the town pump warning the locals not to buy, seize or take possession of any of Madocks' lands, goods or chattels because of contempt to the King and Court of Great Sessions of August 1811. A separate problem appeared in the shape of a notice posted on the embankment wall and on the front door of Tan-yr-Allt. This announced that the real estate was in the hands of Joseph Madocks and Alexander Murray while Samuel Girdlestone now owned all of Madocks' personal estate and was tenant of Tan-yr-Allt. In a bizarre twist, a gardener from Boston appeared with 'vines and pineapples and a vast quantity of fruit trees.' Bricklayers came from Lincolnshire, their foreman reporting, 'We have dug good clay and turned it once over which is very best clay for the Purpose of Making Bricks that can be but now we are at a stand for we want two men . . . And concerning our money we are at a stand for it which I think it very unpleasant that we should not have our money as we ought to do . . ." One of the Welsh contractors wrote, 'We are Willing to Work but we can not work without meat and we Can not get Meat without Money."

A schedule of workmen's demands from October 21st 1811 revealed a sum of £1,094 owing.

Griffith Parry, carpenter, reported that the embankment was now wearing away on the sea side.

William Davies, a cousin of John Williams, who was in charge of re-building on the Penrhyn side reported from Boston Lodge that he had never seen such high spring tides but men were working hard. The price of oats and other foodstuffs was high.

At the end of April the weather had improved but the finances had worsened. 'There is Bailiffs in the house from both parties,' wrote Pace, '. . . the post bringing nothing, the Men struck at Noon & came to the Town . . . I tried to pacify them. They went back to work but stopped again at 3.30 pm and I am very much afraid will not return again till you come home & they are thoroughly settled & paid, the times here are severe & very hard, there was a many crying & making their complaints. . .'

John Williams was away in London, staying at Madocks' rooms in Conduit Street. He was listing assets, valuing, answering demanding correspondence and hoping that those he had left in charge of the embankment repair were succeeding. The breach was still there. As soon as stone was tipped in, much of it was swept away by the tides. Pace had written with the appeal, '. . . if possible do pray keep sending as near as you can to the men's weekly subsist until you come for there is many of them actually starving.'

Griffith Parry however reported work proceeding, '. . . on Thursday evening, we shall put One more Stilt up 23 feet further forward. Now our Waggon's discharge over the very middle of the Gully. The distance at low water from the End of our platform is to the other side 27 yards the depth in the middle of the Gully from 20 to 22 & the Axact distance between the projected Balks is 19 yards and I was determined by the Blessing of God to put the Bridge over it by this day week . . . Send us a good deal of money little will not do the men are quite hard of promises they will not listen to what I can say — how sorry I am that things are so miserable amongst us.' The following morning only a dozen men came to work. Parry wrote, 'We can do no good with so few.'

The high tides returned. Pace reported that one tide was, '. . . almost as high as the one which broke the Bank. The bridge went . . . Such a force of Tides, I never saw them so rapid & with such vengeance.'

John Williams was back in his office. It was raining hard outside. Pace and Jim stood beside him, staring gloomily at the downpour outside.

"This is the end," said Pace.

"We might have one final solution," said Jim, who was of a more positive cast of mind.

A workman passed the window, a sack over his shoulder.

"The breach can be filled if we sink a boat in it carrying ballast," said Jim.

"A boat," said John, "what boat? We have no boat."

"Yes, we have," replied Jim, "We have the *Anne.*"

John looked at Jim in some surprise. This was a special boat, a ketch, dedicated to his wife, and the first boat to be built in this harbour. It had been made with love and care, with no expense spared.

On the other hand, the situation was desperate. The rain continued to fall and the wind was rising. John recognised that in one action they might be able to solve the problem, once and for all. He would not tell his wife until it was all over. He instructed that the plan should be put in action.

The ropes holding the ketch were unfastened. She rose up and down, heavily, in the waves. Three experienced sailors on board manoeuvred her main sail and she turned in the direction of the missing centre of the great embankment. She pitched and rolled but her hands held her firm as she tossed about.

There was no room to stand comfortably on board for in four hours through the day six trolleys of granite had been dumped into her. Just enough to weigh her down but at the same time allow her to sail.

The sky darkened. Spume flew as sea-water collided with the embankment.

John had issued an instruction that three sailors should be onboard, two of them equipped with large axes. When the position was right and the ketch lay across the breach, they were to attack the planking fore and aft. They were to make holes to let in seawater and make their escape across the rocks on both sides.

It was a dangerous proceeding. But the men were desperate to see an end to the months of work.

The storm abated for half-an-hour and the *Anne* rose and fell, sideways to the breach, as if waiting her fate. The light faded.

An unusual, even sound came from the direction of the sea. The three sailors looked out to sea. A grey strip lay over the horizon. A large wave approaching. Two of them took up their stations, fore and aft, and the mainsail, half raised, stretched to its utmost.

The wave struck. The ketch rose, heaved up by the huge volume of water. It shifted sideways. It descended into the breach. A wall of water rose above it. The ketch disappeared. The three sailors were swept overboard. The ketch sunk.

Onlookers from the embankment saw a body rise in the water. In the light of the moon they saw a pale face and an axe twisting in the wind, its metal flashing.

The onlookers on the embankment withdrew, in fear of their lives.

John Williams was watching from the end of the embankment. He saw little except mist and spray.

As the frightened workers passed him, they announced, "We've lost them. Swept away. Very large wave. Took the boat. Men gone."

The following morning, John walked alone along the embankment. The storm had subsided and the wind was a low breeze. He looked into the central section. His boat had sunk across the hole. Its foremast was visible above the water-line, its main sail raggedly floating from it, rising and falling.

Three days later, a body was discovered lying head down in a cove on Ynys Cyngar. Ten yards away, an axe was half buried in the sand.

The bodies of the other two sailors were never found.

Chapter 28

The deaths of the three men in the hideous storm was the talk of Eifionnydd. It was spoken of in cottages, distant farms, after church and chapel and especially in pubs, where accounts became colourful. Those who were on the embankment and witnessed the tragedy described the scene to rapt and horrified attention. 'Given their lives' was a phrase commonly heard. The event had the strange effect of galvanising commitment and effort. Men came back to work and set about with a kind of revenge. These three lives were not to be wasted. The job was to be finished. And at both ends of the broken causeway, men worked with renewed vigour, urging the horses onwards, hauling wagons, tipping the slate and granite into the gap, atop of the unfortunate but sacrificed *Anne*, which had secured itself to the under-footings, the sharp rocks having breached her planking, holding her securely underwater. Her solitary mast became surrounded by stone until it was completely covered.

It may have been that the task would have been less arduous had not most of the iron rails disappeared. And had Richard Williams been in the area, he would most likely have preserved and protected them. But he was not there. His man Caradog was in charge of the smithy in Tremadog. Richard had moved away. He was now living in Bontnewydd, Ruabon. He had accepted a new job. Tom Jones had spoken to him one late afternoon as the last batch of iron rails were being lifted on to the cart bound for Chester.

"Richard," he said, "I need help. This place is busy and successful but I cannot fully cope. I have orders to keep us busy for the next two years. The railways are expanding and rails need making. I have a manager but he is a working man, not a thinker. Not an organiser. You are a leader. Will you join me? I believe you are the man for the job."

Richard stood still for half a minute. He looked at Tom with a full gaze.

"Are you sure?" he replied, surprised but flattered. This iron works was on a large scale. It needed skill and organisation to run it. The great Telford viaduct had been finished a few years earlier, with its huge iron framework, and this had set the standard for major engineering and iron work.

He thought of his father and mother on the farm and his happy times in Tremadog.

"How much will you pay me," he asked.

"Double what you are earning now," was the succinct reply.

That clinched it. The two men shook hands.

He would move over to live here. Elinor and family would have a better life. And he would have challenge and respect in his new position.

Late in 1811, he had moved to his new house, stone-built, detached, with two acres of land, within a stone's throw of the River Dee. His father and mother were both disappointed and pleased.

His son. John Williams was born on the 3rd of May 1812.

When Richard and Elinor returned to Tremadog some eight years later, the Rhos ironworks was in decline and Tom Jones in severe difficulties. One of the Wilkinson brothers was in dispute with him.

Two of Richard and Elinor's sons were on the threshold of distinction. William was to become the founder member of the Festiniog Railway Company, owing to his expertise in iron and engineering, and John, although staying as a blacksmith for the rest of his life, was a Welsh-language poet, (under the bardic name of Ioan Madog), winning prizes in Eisteddfodau, famous for his facility with *cynghanedd*, those intricate, chiming, verse-forms.

Chapter 29

Death, again, was to occupy the neighbourhood.

People gathered at street corners in small groups. The word 'murder' hung in the air.

This concerned an unfortunate servant-girl called Mary Jones at a farm just above the Penrhyn end of the embankment. One of the men working on completing the Embankment had decided to steal from the house, believing that all were out working in the fields. He was Thomas Edwards, a 6' 2" giant called 'King of the Mountains' or (worse) 'The Great South Walian' *('Hwntwr Mawr')*. He had killed the young lady in a fit of panic when discovered stealing in the farmhouse. He was discovered digging up his loot in a sheep-fold. He escaped his pursuers, crossing Traeth Bach (the course of the River Dwyryd) below Portmeirion. Six constables were appointed to take him to Dolgellau by night. He complained that the straps securing him were too tight, escaped, and was re-captured in woods near Penrhyndeudraeth. In the court of great Sessions in 1813, David Ellis-Nanney was the prosecuting counsel.

In September 1812 an unusual party occupied the Madoc Arms. The poet Shelley was in residence, with his young wife Harriet, looking for a place to live and a place to exercise his taste for radical thinking. John Williams thought they were ideal as tenants of Tan-yr-Allt and he wrote suggesting this to Girdlestone, who now owned the property.

He replied, in some concern: 'With respect to Mr Shelley, however good his connection may be, they do not seem at present much to avail him He being himself under age, no security he can give, will be all binding . . . I am afraid that Mr S would by no means prove the sort of Tenant that wd. Be

114

useful to us. A young man who has, I suspect, married beneath him, & therefore offended his family . . . You must take special care to not let Mr. Shelley into possession of the house or if he gets in, we may have great difficulties in getting him out again."

But the young poet said that he wanted to invest a good sum of money in the embankment. And John Williams had no other tenant.

Shelley threw himself with alacrity into schemes for raising money for finishing the embankment. Unfortunately, not for the first time, he blotted his copy-book by being run in for debt in Caernarfon, from which he removed himself through payment of bail.

Beaumaris was to hold a meeting in aid of the embankment. 'Many gentlemen of respectability' were to be there. Toasts were drunk and Shelley made an impassioned speech for ". . . this great, this glorious cause." The subscription list reached an amazing £1,185, with Shelley promising £100, which of course he never paid.

Tan-yr-Allt was leased to Percy Bysshe at an annual rent of £100, with the option of paying it when he came of age and came in to his fortune.

Shelley wrote to Williams: '. . . my fervid hopes, my ardent desires, my unremitting personal exertions (as far as my health will allow) are all engaged in that cause, which I will desert but with my life. Can you hire me a trustworthy maid-servant as we shall require three in all . . .'

The Shelleys arrived in Tremadog in mid-November. He wrote that Tan-yr-Allt was '. . . a cottage extensive and tasty enough for the villa of an Italian Prince.' He did work. He spent time in the embankment office writing, asking for money, and he rode about the countryside in such a search.

The Poet and his very young wife were so settled into Tan-yr-Allt that they felt free to criticise Madocks and his guests. She wrote, 'We are now living in his house where formerly nothing but folly and extravagance reigned . . . Here they held midnight revels insulting the spirit of Nature's sublime scenery . . .'

Three years later, Harriet was dead, drowned in the Serpentine.·

Percy Bysshe was working on a new extended poem. *Queen Mab.* In it, this pretentious teenager expounds the history of the world and the causes of its miserable state. 'Kings, priests and statesmen' get the worst of it, marriage and commerce come off badly, and love will conquer all. Scribbling away in Tanny, the Poet was having problems with his ink. The cold of the 1812/13 winter had driven through the house, with its many thin-glass windows, like a knife.

The Welsh came in for severe criticism. Although Harriet Shelley and Mrs Ellis-Nanney played duets together, otherwise they made few friends. After a few weeks, he announced, "Welsh society is very stupid . . . They are all aristocrats or saints . . . more philosophy in one square inch of any tradesman's counter than in the whole of Cambria.

On 3rd of March, 1813, Shelley dashed off the following lines to his publisher: 'Tan-yr-Allt. Dear Sir, I have just escaped an atrocious assassination. Oh send me £20 if you have it! You will perhaps hear of me no more! Your friend PERCY SHELLEY.'

An account by Harriet seems to hold the truth. She writes from Dublin on March 11: 'We arrived here last Tuesday . . . Mr S. promised you a recital of the horrible events that caused us to leave Wales . . . everything that can recall to his mind the horrors of that night.

'On Friday night, the 26th February, we retired to bed between ten and eleven o'clock. We had been in bed about half-an-hour, when Mr S. heard a noise proceeding from one of the parlours. He immediately went downstairs with two pistols, which he had loaded that night, expecting to have occasion for them. He went into the billiard room, where he had heard footsteps retreating; he followed into another little room, which we called an office. He there saw a man in the act of quitting the room through a glass window which opens into the shrubbery. The man fired at Mr S. which he avoided. Bysshe then fired, but it flashed in the pan. The man knocked Bysshe down, and they struggled on the ground. Bysshe then fired his second pistol, which he thought wounded him in the shoulder, as he uttered a shriek and got up, when he said these words: "By God, I will be revenged! I will murder your wife; I will ravish your sister! By God. I will be revenged!" He then fled as we hoped for the night . . . We all assembled in the parlour, where we remained for two hours. Mr S. then advised us to retire, thinking it impossible that he would make a second attack. We left Bysshe and the manservant, who had only arrived that day . . . I had been in bed three hours when I heard a pistol go off. I immediately ran downstairs, when I perceived that Bysshe's flannel gown had been shot through, and the window curtain. Bysshe had sent Daniel to see what the hour it was, when he heard a noise at the window. He went there, and a man thrust his arm through the glass and fired at him. Thank Heaven! The ball went through his gown and he remained unhurt. Mr S. happened to stand sideways; had he stood fronting, the ball must have killed him. Bysshe fired his pistol but it would not go off; he then aimed a blow at him with an old sword, which we found in the house. The assassin attempted to get the sword from him, and just as he was pulling it away, Dan rushed into the room, when he made his escape.

This was four in the morning. It had been a most dreadful night; the wind was loud as thunder, and the rain descended in torrents . . . H. Shelley.'

Harriet blamed a Mr Leeson who ' . . . has been heard to say that he was determined to drive us out of the country . . .' and that he had said it was all a made-up incident by Mr S. so that he could leave the area quickly without paying his bills.

But that of course is what he did. They decamped to Dublin, quickly.

Several years later, David Ellis-Nanney was still sorting out the debts left behind by 'that ungrateful fellow.'

As a postscript to this sorry tale of adventure, attempted murder and debt, especially debt, Madocks wrote to John Williams: 'I want to return home sadly, but my pocket is dreadfully low. I wish you could somehow contrive to send me ten pounds. Even five pounds would do, and I will contrive to return it in about a fortnight when Mr John arrives . . . Direct to me Post Office, Chester.' But before the money had time to reach him, he wrote to John two days later: 'Pray send over my Grey-mare to Barmouth early Thursday morning, and some sort of horse by the same man to take my portmanteau to Tre Madoc . . . You need not send the money now to Chester, as I have borrowed enough to take me to Barmouth, or rather a Gentleman is giving me a lift . . .'

Later, in London for the opening of Parliament, Madocks complained of gout and rheumatism: '. . . the old enemy . . .' He asks for some small rents . . . 'by return of post. I am wretchedly ill. Confined at the Coach House Hotel, Hatchett's, Piccadilly without a single comfort. I was never so wretched. But do not let my sufferings be known. I will bear up & write next week. Deduct the ten pounds for Godsake send me up the Rents. Direct them to Albany, Piccadilly. Yrs my dear John / Most miserably / & in greatest pain / W.A.M.'

But the Grand Scheme was intact in his mind. His planner's intellect was in good order: 'I assure you that I employ my mind incessantly in thinking how to compass those important objects necessary to complete the system of improvements in Snowdonia, and one of which wanting, the rest lose half their value. If I can give them birth, shape and substance before I die, they will work their own way to posterity ... If it does not advance, it will recede. It will not be stationary like the mountains around it.'

In need of a wife, as Jane Austen said. Looking to mid Wales, Madocks' fortunes were about to change.

Chapter 30

And in the Borough, as Madocks grandly called it, there were improvements. John Williams kept his hand on the tiller and the till. He was, through his rent-collector, who was usually his brother, firm but sensible with tenants. If they could not pay all of this week's rent this week, the balance was held over until next week. There was a great deal of coming-and-going among the men of the households. Sometimes they worked here, on the embankment or on building houses, and sometimes they worked in farms where their full board and lodging was covered for weeks. They'd come home, and the rent, including arrears, was paid.

Diligent, industrious and fair, John Williams saw to it that the Tan-yr-Allt Estate, as originally bought by Madocks, which incidentally included all of the land which the later-named Porthmadog sat on, produced all the income it was meant to. Some properties had been mortgaged and Tan-yr-Allt was in legal limbo because its apparent owner was languishing in a London jail. So, even though Tan-yr-Allt had been lost as an asset of the original estate, many of the other premises, especially in Tremadog, built with Madocks' capital, remained, and rentals accrued.

In 1814, the breach was healed and the Cob patched-up. Many of the best stonemasons had left for other jobs, but the faithful Twm remained. He was still hard-working, still cared for the quality of the work, and anything John Williams wanted done, Twm would see to it. The bond between the two men was remarkable and was never broken. It was Twm who supervised the final laying of a fine-stone tarred surface across the top of the Embankment. There was room for a railway (much talked of but never achieved in those early days) and there was room for carriages and walkers. Tolls were set, honest men employed and Madocks began to enjoy a regular income.

By this time, in his forties, he was no sprightly young man. But he delighted in his 'Borough.' He came over there in between his Parliamentary duties and was seen about the streets, raising his stick, examining the stonework, checking water-flow, and especially traversing his Cob, of which he was very proud.

Although his old spirit never deserted him, he always had the schemes, the vision, the demand for action now — he was somewhat worn, somewhat slower. His gout had not improved; it does not. Some days he lay in bed, in pain.

But he had much to live for, he reflected one day in 1817. Much of his health was fine. His brain was good. His men were working for him, in the Borough, in Parliament and in Boston, for he had ever the gift of attracting loyalty.

He decided that he would take the waters in Bath. It was the fashionable thing and you never know, it might do his health some good. And the health of his mind (and perhaps the health of his pocket too.) He might find a wife, and, best of all, a wife with money to invest. Bath was the place.

He had a good look at his clothes in his Conduit Street, London, rooms. He put some items aside, as being rather worn, and others somewhat out-of-fashion. As he walked up the steps to his tailors, clutching the black iron hand-rail, he felt that two new breeches and two coats would suit him nicely, one in smoky brown. Also a couple of Irish cotton shirts, one in pale pink, and some scarves, one dark blue one. Two new pairs of shoes were essential and in another street he had himself measured for these.

So the time came when, with two sizeable valises, he boarded the westward carriage. Overnight was pleasant; some good company and a roast duck. The second night, in Bristol, he met some very clever people who were set on making large amounts of money. And when Bath hove in sight, with the traceried rise of Bath Abbey high in the sky, he felt a strong liftening of spirits. A brisk young man carried his bags to the Royal Crescent, with its thirty tall colonnaded residences, many for short-term rent, and a fine view over the city, where a dutiful orderly smiled in gratitude at his presence and showed him to his rooms, which were agreeable if not luxurious.

His first visit was to the Pump Room. In its large, elegant hall he took the waters, sipping them not too enthusiastically because they tasted foul. Conversations drew the information that that night, at the Assembly Building, there was an event of quality dancing in the Room with professional musicians and lavish catering.

The early evening saw him unpacking his smoky-brown coat from the sideboard and when he checked himself in the long mirror, he pronounced himself pleased. He had not entirely lost the darkness in his hair and his shoes were thin and well-made.

The Assembly Rooms had their important social function. Pleasure and utility went hand-in-hand. Securing a suitable mate was of more than personal importance. It engaged with property and position, continuity and security. Madocks, despite his financial difficulties of late (and of course he would minimise his debts and maximise his assets), still had his Tan-yr-Allt estate, where now children were being born, a school established, its inhabitants soon to refer to their new town as 'Porthmadog,' named after him.

He looked around the room and was very impressed. Fresh white paint lay on the large doors and their frames, the oak floor was polished, walls were in pale blue, punctuated by white friezes. Chandeliers hung from the ceiling. A quadrille was in progress, the movement smooth, the orchestra in a good state of co-operation. Three young ladies threw him glances and urged him forward with "Come on.

Come on. Join us." Hands were thrown forward and he held two of them as they all moved sideways then forwards. He was a quick learner and he was enjoying himself.

"Mr Madocks," said one, as he sat beside her. He could not recall that he had mentioned his name. "How very nice to see you. You must be new here. What a fine time we are all having," and she threw a glance at her two companions, one of whom was her sister.

"Very fine," he replied, somewhat out-of-breath. He did notice that most of the men dancing were younger than himself. However, he crossed his legs and straightened his back and determined that he was as good a match as anybody. Many of the young men did seem rather odd, with foppish hair and a swerving, dipping, manner. Sometimes a loud laugh, resembling that of a mule, emerged from a group of young men.

He was admiring the skill of how the wooden floor had been laid when he saw an ankle. More than an ankle. Two ankles and the base of two nicely-turned legs. They moved with a smooth unison and clearly belonged to a skilled dancer. Every now and then there was a little kick, which Madocks found exciting. He lost interest in his companion, who spoke something but he did not reply.

As he looked upwards he saw a young lady of rare manner. Her bearing was controlled yet easy. She raised her arms with precision. They were dressed in long brown gloves. How odd that I should have chosen brown, he thought. She was youthful yet attractively mature. She showed interest in her companion as she danced although there was a guarded formality about her. Her shoes were black delicate pumps and her light yellow dress was covered by a cashmere shawl.

Madocks tried not to stare but the lady had seen his attention. At a break in the dancing, he stood up and before the lady had time to withdraw, he stepped into her path.

"May I have the next dance?" he enquired.

"Certainly," she replied.

Closer to her, he noticed that she wore an exquisite tippet of swans' down around her neck.

This time, it was a cotilion. He managed the moving, around and forward, although he had never done this before.

"A little new?" she enquired.

"Yesterday," he replied. "I took the coach from London. You?" he enquired.

"Wales." she replied decisively.

"Wales, too," replied Madocks. "I have an estate in the north west."

She raised her head in surprise and looked at him more intently. Something about this man attracted her. There was a happiness in him, although he was little in the matter of masculinity compared with some specimens in the room.

They danced with style and confidence. Where he was a little unsure, he chanced his arm. They sat and talked. He found it easy. She was full of detail about her home near Brecon, how the farms were well-handled, the gardens supplying fruit and vegetables, the staff in the house friendly and caring. All this was music to Madocks' ears.

After the break, the musicians broke into a waltz. He had new confidence. Freely, he took her by the hand and waist and without too much vigour at first, guided her in circular paths over the polished floor. She was smiling.

Two days later, he withdrew from Bath in a haze of pleasure. Tregunter, Breconshire, was next on his list of calling-places.

Chapter 31

On the second of April, 1818, William Alexander Madocks married the elaborately named Amelia Sophia Hughes (her father's name) at Tregunter, Breconshire.

He wrote to John Williams:-

Gloucester

Wednesday Eve

My Dear John,

I am all aground. I have arrived so late the Bank is shut up and the accommodation is hopeless till tomorrow morning, so I may as well take up my pen to reassure you, that we shall be at Tany Bwlch, Thursday evening, the 2nd of July, and make our Grand Entrée, as you propose, on Friday, into Tre Madoc. As you feel equally alive to it as myself, I need not enjoin you to prepare. Only let me Urge the removal of the Gravel Bank in front of Ynys Towyn. The Flag Staff. Borrow some flags from Pwlhelly. Get 2 or 3 or 4 harpers. A few bottles of White wine from Caernarvon. The Flag Staff at the North Sluice. The cannons in the Rocks. You may depend on our being at Tany Bwlch the 2nd of July, Thursday, tomorrow week.

Do not ask Mr Nanney or Miss Jones or anybody to break in on us at dinner the first day. Let the Dinner be Snug & we can repair after the Illuminations. All the rest of the plan holds good. The Dinner at the town, Freeholders Ball in the Town Hall etc. Illuminations etc. You will hear from me again about the line of March from Tany Bwlch. I mean all the plan to remain as we settled except as to the Dinner at Ynys y Towyn, where we had rather that first day be alone among ourselves. That is 3 ladies, myself, as we can then stroll on the Bank after dinner etc., without interruption, or form, before the Ball & the Illuminations.

Let the Nursery Walks etc. be swept and weeded.

I am sure, my dear John, you will do the best to give effect to a day which, if anything can restore Tre Madoc, that will — You may put Mrs Madocks name down for £10 a year to the School, which she will present that day. All the children of the school should join in the procession.

I know you will make a good thing & produce an effect, so I will leave all the rest to you, with the hints I have given. Borrow plenty of Flags from Pwlhelly & Caernarfon. Detain a Captain or two, & fill the Port.

Prepare a Horse or two to meet us at Dolgelly, if necessary. I summon you to that effect. We shall bring plate and Servants.

Relying on your Zeal to make a great day for Tre Madoc. Believe me.

Yours Ever
Most Sincerely
W.A.M.

[The letter continued]

Do not open any of my packages by the Vessel, till I arrive.

Neither you nor I shall have Tre Madoc comfortable, till that is done . . . It is not possible for me to bring Ladies to such a neighbourhood. Some sort of decency and respect must be kept up . . . Respectability is of much consequence at Tre Madoc & the Colony as Rental. Depend on it the prosperity of the place depends on it. [Here the letter ends.]

In 1820 William's brother Joseph died, leaving no issue. Again, William's luck with inheritance applied and he inherited £8,000.

In 1821 the population of Tremadog (which included all

that segment later called Porthmadog) was a healthy 885 and rapidly increasing.

Madocks knew that a good half of the Great Scheme was completed but he was keen to get on with the rest of it. This involved the efficient carriage of slate down from the quarries in Blaenau Ffestiniog, lifting them on to boats and sailing them away for use in distant places, all for profit. At present slates were transported by mule, horse and cart, to the Dwyryd River at Traeth Bach. Here they were loaded on to flat-bottomed boats or barges and floated downriver to the wider estuary where the slates (a dangerous activity) were lifted on to sea-going vessels. Madocks recognised the clumsiness of this procedure and proposed bringing the slates to Traeth Mawr, crossing them over the new Cob and storing them on the Port quayside, where they would be shipped out. This was now becoming possible because the Glaslyn was continuing to scoop out a hole suitable for the new docks and quayside, where freight-carrying ships could dock.

The Port Madoc Harbour Bill was going through Parliament; it marked the name of the new town, and the plan for the new slates route. By Michaelmas 1824 the Port harbour was ready to receive vessels of up to 60 tons. Madocks had a feisty correspondence on the matter of Griffith Griffiths and his four sons, who were to work on the harbour walls and the buildings. The area known as 'Pen Cei' was causing problems: 'Pray let me know if Griffith Griffiths keeps the new Southern Quay out enough in the River as the Companies not, as many rocks are left in the Channel which will prevent ships coming alongside the Quay . . . Griffiths must not hug the Garth too much to save his pocket.' Opposite this section of wharf (where Ioan Madog later had his workshop) some decades later an island rose out of the water, called Ballast Island, formed by rocks thrown overboard by schooners returning from trans-ocean voyages.

One large house, Morva Lodge, overlooking the new town and harbour, was not enough for Madocks. He wanted two, the second one for John Williams, Land Agent and now dubbed Director of Works for the Town and Harbour of Porth Madog.

Ty Hwnt i'r Bwlch meant 'The other side of the Gap,' a name understandable only when the old landscape, before Madocks, is envisaged; the gap being the eastern flanks of Moel y Gest through which travellers on foot came from the Criccieth direction. They paid a toll to the local landowner. The old farmhouse was altered and a handsome two story house emerged, with a spectacular view. As John walked on the front lawn he observed the growing town at his feet, with Snowdon to the left in the distance and swerving away below him, ending at the Glaslyn's entrance-point, the long line of the first embankment. He recalled the night when he sweated away, digging and throwing, in the pouring rain, to raise its level and keep the sea out. This was perhaps a portent of the later embankment collapse, but the outcome, after much physical determination, was a successful one.

Madocks' larger house, Morva Lodge, with its stone gateposts, off the road to Morfa Bychan, also had a second entrance, flanked by a gatehouse, from the road to Criccieth, just off Porthmadog's High Street. Following the symmetry, John Williams created a second gatehouse and a second drive, leading upwards in parallel to the first, to Ty Hwnt i'r Bwlch. It could be said that the two houses were as brothers or partners, symbolising unity, similarity and loyalty.

The two houses were some two hundred yards apart, high on each side of the hill, built of large local stone. Morva Lodge had a tall wing where guests could emerge from their beds to admire the new town and harbour below. It had a slated outstretched partial roof around the rest of the building, echoing the overhanging veranda roof at Tan-yr-Allt. It had a brass hand-rail (reminiscent of boat-building) curving up the inside wall of the enclosed central staircase.

The combined views from both houses were a panorama, stretching from the Eryri Mountains on the left, over all of Traeth Mawr and the Cob, to Cardigan Bay on the far right. Both houses were as sentinels, signalling the creativity and achievement of two extraordinary men working in partnership, guarding their legacy then and now.

Besides their two similar houses, both men had other matters in common. Both were parents of a child born in the same year, a boy for the Williamses (called W.T. Massey Williams, born 1822) and a girl for the Madocks (called Eliza Anne Maria Ermine Madocks, born 1822).

John Williams inevitably became involved in surveying the direction of a railway line from the slate quarries up in Blaenau (about twelve miles away) down (through a drop of some eight hundred feet) to the shore. A surveyor called William Provis presented a scheme at Tremadog on the 12th of December 1825 which formed the basis for the line that was eventually built by the Festiniog Railway Company.

Morva Lodge was a favourite of Mrs Madocks and her daughter. John Etheridge was appointed caretaker and as usual he received a spate of letters telling him what to do: 'Have dinner at all events at 6 o'clock on Tuesday, namely, a joint of Mutton roasted. One boiled Chicken and one roast Duck, and a Rice Pudding. If we do not come by four o'clock by Tuesday keep the things till Friday . . . .Before you put the hangings on the best bed in the Bow Window Room, Sleep in it on the feather bed and bolsters to air it well and it should be put in the sun if the weather is hot and fine . . . We bring a cook but want a cleanly girl to wash the dishes. Do not get Mrs Roberts from Penmorfa. She will not do at all. Some clean young person. I hope the flag will be flying from the Tower if large enough. If not, get one from the Ships. I hope to get a cask of porter from Daniel. Williams lends feather beds and blankets . . . I hope the Dove is arrived & that the looking-glass will be put over the chimney in the Dining Room. There must be 2 servants beds over the stable . . . .'

Cuttings and plants were exchanged from the garden at Morva Lodge to Tregunter. A conservatory was erected and grapes grown. A melon frame was knocked together. 'The fruit is so great an object to my Ladies, and I find they miss fruit in North Wales more than anything else. They are remarkably fond of it . . . I am much pleased to find you take so much care of Morva Lodge . . . as Mrs Madocks is very fond of it, and, Please God, we shall be there a great deal the next Summer.'

On 31 May, 1826, Mr Madocks, his wife, his daughter and his step-daughter, landed at Le Havre, en route for Italy via France and Switzerland. In June they were in Paris. They headed for Geneva and in early winter they were in Florence. In May 1827 they were in Rome and then in Naples. Here they occupied the second floor of the Gran Brettagna Hotel for the sum of 640 ducats. Their accommodation included 'Breakfast with fruit, Dinner, and tea in the evening for four Masters, board for the young Lady and her Governess, the board for 4 servants, 60 wax candles, that is 2 a day, a lamp with oil and a Carriage.' On payment of one ducat per head, friends could be brought in for dinner, a maximum of three at a time.

William had North Wales much on his mind. His correspondence with John Williams continued. He said he would be back in July.

His daughter was also a letter-writer. She wrote to Master Williams, Ynys Towyn:-

Dear Little John,

I hope you are as well as I am. I write this at the foot of a great smoking mountain almost as high as Snowdon, sometimes it throws out fire from the top. I hope soon to be in Wales and shall be glad to see Morva Lodge and Port Madoc again; and all the ships. Remember me to Mr & Mrs Williams and believe me to remain always

Yours sincerely

Eliza Anna Maria Ermine Madocks

PS: I should like to see the new school.

The river Glaslyn was still flowing the wrong way. Correspondence between Madocks and John concerned ways in which the river could be re-directed. Madocks was keen to get all of Traeth Mawr drained and revenues rolling in.

In March 1828 they were in Rome. Morva Lodge was on Madocks' mind and he wrote to Etheridge: '. . . I mean the Paper with little Birds on a flower pattern. Put this in the Drawing Room (the room that looks to Towyn). Put all round the room above the Dado only; & below the dado to be the present paper light green . . . Put also the Bird paper upon the ceiling under the arch by the East window. You can cut the paper so as not to injure the prints upon the walls . . . Messrs Morlands will send you some more money . . . Stock the garden well for July & Aug. Plenty of Peas & Beans & Lettuces . . . . How are the strawberries and raspberries?'

News came from Williams of the turning of the river, but this was temporary and to this day the river runs against the Minffordd shore. In his last surviving letter to John, Madocks says: 'I am much gratified by your letter of 30th of March . . . God Bless you & God Prosper the Colony!!! Amen! Ever yrs. Mo. Affectly, W. A. Madocks.' In this letter he discusses details of the river bed and referred to a map of the Iron Rail Way.

The family travelled through Italy, across Switzerland and France to Paris. They moved in to No. 109, Faubourg Saint-Honore, Paris.

There, William Madocks died. The fatal date was September 15, 1828.

His body stayed in France, not, as it ought to have been, buried in a vault (as John Williams and his wife were) in St. John's Church, Tremadog.

He was buried on September 17, 1828, at Pere Lachaise cemetery, Paris.

He is not one of the famous people buried there. His grave, in the old English section, is neglected, its inscription gone. A tree grows through it. Perhaps a fitting emblem to the growth he created and left behind in his beloved Eifionnydd. After him, the railway fired up and the slate industry multiplied. Tremadog and Porthmadog grew commercially and socially.

Tremadog has his image, healthy and theatrical and smiling, on a round plaster 'lozenge' attached to the façade of the central building, first designed for the community, a meeting-place, for drama, musical events and eisteddfodau. In the centre of the square there is a plinth. On it stands a meagre metal stem holding a lamp. Madocks' effigy should be here, in everlasting granite, both arms raised to encompass Blaenau Ffestiniog, where slate was dug out of mountains, and the town and harbour of Porthmadog which he created, from where slate was exported in locally-built schooners, crewed by brave sailors, across vast distances.

He had 'lost' a huge sum of money; in the region of £80,000. But 'invested' might be a better term. Very few people on this earth can be credited with such a rich legacy. He founded two towns, a community of diligent, hard-working, people, and laid the foundations for a prosperity in slate and shipping that was to expand hugely through the nineteenth and into the twentieth century.

He drew strength and inspiration from a long line of ancestors in the fertile Vale of Clwyd. The name Madog appears in the early family tree. The first to use Madocks was John Madocks of Bodfari, Esquire (1601–62). They were successful land-owners, farmers, traders, soldiers. John

Madocks, William's father and successful London lawyer, created the wealth which his son used. They served their community as Squire, Sherif and Burgess. Their six hundred years of continuity and William Madocks' work with the seductive Glaslyn reflect the Madocks family motto

NOT FOR MYSELF ALONE.